EXCITING PIECES

● *I went out to Charing Cross, to see Major-general Harrison hanged, drawn, and quartered, which was done there, he looking as cheerful as any man could do in that condition.*

(Samuel Pepys)

THE
TEACHER'S RELIEF BOOK

The Teacher's Relief Book

Devised by Jay Heale.

– FENROSE –

FENROSE

First Edition 1973
Published by Fenrose, Ltd.,
21 Mount Ephraim Road,
Tunbridge Wells, Kent.

Illustrations by Richard Ayres
Typesetting by Amigo Graphics Centre, Ltd.
Printed photolitho in Great Britain by
Ebenezer Baylis & Son Limited,
The Trinity Press, Worcester and London

Selection and arrangement © 1973 Jay Heale

ISBN 0 903879 02 6

Contents

Explanatory Preamble

> I have known colleagues, with the kindest (but most deplorable) intentions, read stories to boys in class the last day or two "after exams". . . . I can conceive of no circumstances whatever under which such things could be even pardonable.
>
> *The Headmaster of a Preparatory School to his Teaching Colleagues* – 1921

Reading aloud has been for years the prerogative of nannies and indulgent parents. Teachers only dared try it when the Headmaster (who taught classics) wasn't around. Nowdays, we are enlightened. We have rediscovered ancient truisms. "Lo!" we say. "They enjoy being read to — and, moreover, it can even be classed as educational." In the midst of their laughter and glee, we rejoice that our pupils actually learn new words, new ideas, new authors.

We appreciate, now, that we ourselves must read carefully whatever authors we intend recommending to those pupils — whether it be Rosemary Sutcliff or William Mayne, Charles Dickens or Feodor Dostoevsky. Equally, we know that we haven't time to read all we should, and precious little time to sort out the best extracts with which to tempt or educate or enliven our young audience.

We have our few treasured pieces which we read regularly to each new class, though even these are sometimes ruined when the bell goes, and it's time for that classically-minded Headmaster again! If only we had worked out in advance just how long that story took to read. . . . .

So this book is an offering to fill the gap. Here are extracts deliberately chosen from adult writers writing for adults. What pleasanter way to be introduced to Dylan Thomas, or "Saki", or

Paul Jennings? Here are some of the "immortals" (though opinions differ!) in the shape of the Cricket Match from "England, their England", "The Unicorn in the Garden" by James Thurber, the closing extracts from Scott's diary. Here, naturally, are tried personal favourites of my own: Stephen Leacock, and "Sapper". There should be something for whatever mood you want, for classes of boys and girls, aged about eleven to fourteen.

Each piece is timed, and many have optional cuts (usually of irrelevant or over-complicated sentences). None of us reads at the same speed, so a glance at page 9 ·will show you how to adjust the timings as necessary.

A second volume is already in preparation. If there are passages so far omitted, and essential, in your view, for future inclusion, I shall be glad to hear from you.

My own personal thanks to my recent colleague, Tom Simpson, for his suggestions and helpful criticisms. His infectious love of reading has enriched the learning of countless pupils and more than several schoolmasters, including myself.

Above all, decided recognition to the boys of Holmewood House, Kent, and of Monterey, Cape, South Africa, who endured my reading aloud to them, and by their reactions justified this book.

JAY HEALE
1973

● *What frenzy has of late possessed the brain !*
  Though few can write, yet fewer can refrain.
(Samuel Garth)

TIMING CHECK

The following lunatic story takes me exactly one and a half minutes to read aloud. Try it yourself, *aloud*, timing it, and you'll know whether you have to add or subtract from my estimates through the book. The timing given does not allow for Title announcement, explanatory diversions, or prolonged rounds of applause. The full reading time is given at the start of each piece: a subsequent figure in square brackets shows the time using the suggested [square-bracketed] cuts.

SIR FRED   1½

One chilly day out of the mists of legend, when swirling winds turned the bare boughs of young oaks into clutching claws, a lonely figure galloped through the wild countryside of Garbistan, coloured pink by the reddening sky. It was a wandering knight named Sir Fred who was searching for adventure. It was hard to find. All the best giants had been killed already by King Arthur and his tableful of Round Knights. Sir Fred had knocked at a few likely-looking castles, but nobody seemed to have any adventures to spare. He had stood so long outside one door that his armour had iced up at the joints, and his horse had to breathe at him hard until he was melted back into action.

Amid the lengthening shadows, he suddenly noticed footprints in the snow, leading towards a yawning cave. At the same instant, from out of the blackness there came a scream for help.

Sir Fred dismounted and made all haste up the slope. In the cave he found a tall and beautiful woman and a green, scaly, blubbering dragon. Sir Fred drew his trusty sword and charged. It was a long desperate struggle, but at length he won, and Sir Fred and the dragon walked out of the gloomy depths side by side, leaving the woman fuming, writhing, and tied up in a corner.

"It was lucky you heard me," said the dragon with a sigh of gratitude. "You arrived only just in time. One more minute and she would have sliced me up and cooked me for supper."

(from "*The Exploits of Fred*")

10

Timing Index

Minutes				Page
9	*The Revenge*	Lord Tennyson	Exciting	127
9	[The Mouse]	"Saki"	Amusing	42
9½	Snapshot of a Dog	James Thurber	Moving	190
10	The Mouse	"Saki"	Amusing	42
10	from God's Smuggler			
	(3 extracts)	Brother Andrew	Moving	193
11	[Sredni Vashtar]	"Saki"	Exciting	135
11	[The Gift of the Magi]	O. Henry	Moving	198
11½	Thousand Pound Pull	Jack London	Exciting	131
12½	[The Truce of the Bear]	"Sapper"	Exciting	139
12½	Sredni Vashtar	"Saki"	Exciting	135
12½	[Ebeneezer the Goat]	"Sapper"	Amusing	50
12	[In the House of Shaws]	R.L. Stevenson	Exciting	149
13	[The Nightingale and the Rose]	Oscar Wilde	Moving	203
13	Memories of Christmas	Dylan Thomas	Amusing	45
13½	Ebeneezer the Goat	"Sapper"	Amusing	50
13½	The Lumber Room	"Saki"	Amusing	55
13½	The Gift of the Magi	O. Henry	Moving	198
14½	The Truce of the Bear	"Sapper"	Exciting	139
14½	The Nightingale and the Rose	Oscar Wilde	Moving	203
15½	Ice Cold	Alistair Maclean	Exciting	144
16½	[Soaked in Seaweed]	Stephen Leacock	Amusing	60
16½	[The Devoted Friend]	Oscar Wilde	Amusing	69
16½	In the House of Shaws	R.L. Stevenson	Exciting	149
17	[Hop-Frog]	E.A. Poe	Exciting	156
17	Nicky's Story	David Wilkerson	Moving	208
19	Hop-Frog	E.A. Poe	Exciting	156
20	Soaked in Seaweed	Stephen Leacock	Amusing	60
21½	The Devoted Friend	Oscar Wilde	Amusing	69
24½	[The Striped Chest]	Sir A. Conan-Doyle	Exciting	164
27	The Striped Chest	Sir A. Conan-Doyle	Exciting	164
33½	[The Cricket Match]	A.G. Macdonell	Amusing	97
34	Knights Errant	T.H. White	Amusing	78
43	The Cricket Match	A.G. Macdonell	Amusing	94

A NOTE ON THE CUTTING

Any form of cutting must obviously spoil the effect of the author's original work. Ideally, the entirety of any prose or poetic passage should be printed, and it should be read in full as well. But this method will rob our pupils of much that they will enjoy and appreciate, for we tend not to choose passages which are obviously too long or too complicated.

So, the "cuts" suggested by square brackets in some of these passages are put there for just those two reasons. Either the original piece may be too long, or it may contain digressions which over-complicate the essential story line.

Without intending any insult to those using this book, I have suggested (in italics within square brackets) a few simplifications of words or phrases which might confuse young listeners. These are often replacements, rather than direct synonyms. My intention, throughout the conception and preparation of this book, has been to make good reading pleasantly available, with the least difficulty, for the maximum enjoyment.

● *Read over your compositions, and where ever you meet with a passage which you think is particularly fine, strike it out.*

(Dr Samuel Johnson)

Acknowledgements

The Editor and Publishers are grateful for permission to reproduce items in this book as follows:

— from "God's Smuggler" by Brother Andrew, used by permission of the publishers, Hodder & Stoughton. Copyright.
— "The Unicorn in the Garden" and "Snapshot of a Dog", both from "Vintage Thurber" by James Thurber, © 1963, Hamish Hamilton, London.
— to The Bodley Head for the stories "The Conjurer's Revenge" from "Literary Lapses", and "Soaked in Seaweed" from "Nonsense Novels" both by Stephen Leacock.
— from "Reynard the Fox" by John Masefield, to the Society of Authors as the literary representative of the Estate of John Masefield.
— to the Bodley Head and The Observer for the use of "UB" from "Oddly Enough", and "The Cheesecake Chore" from "Oodles of Oddlies".
— for ·"Memories of Christmas" from "Quite Early One Morning" by Dylan Thomas, used by permission of J.M. Dent & Sons Ltd., and the Trustees for the Copyrights of the late Dylan Thomas.
— "Ebeneezer the Goat" and "The Truce of the Bear" from "Sapper's War Stories" by permission of the Estate of the late H.C. McNeile, and A.P. Watt & Son.
— from "H.M.S. Ulysses" by Alistair Maclean, used by permission of Collins, Publishers.
— from "The Cross and the Switchblade" by David Wilkerson and John Sherrill, used by permission of David Wilkerson Youth Crusades.
— "The Striped Chest" from "The Conan Doyle Stories" by Sir A. Conan-Doyle, used by permission of John Murray (Publishers) Ltd. and Baskerville Investments Ltd.
— from "The Sword in the Stone" by T.H. White, used by permission of David Higham Associates, Ltd.
— from "England, their England" by A.G. Macdonell, used by permission of Macmillan, London and Basingstoke.

AMUSING

AMUSING PIECES

*The Prothero Fire is an episode taken
from Memories of Christmas

†King Pellinore's Joust is an episode taken
from Knights Errant

● *"Contrariwise,"* continued *Tweedledee, "if it was so, it might be; and if it were so, it would be; but as it isn't, it ain't. That's logic."*
(Charles Lutwidge Dodgson)

THE TIRED WOMAN'S EPITAPH

Anonymous   1

Here lies a poor woman who always was tired:
She lived in a house where help was not hired.
Her last words on earth were:"Dear friends, I am going
Where washing ain't done, nor sweeping nor sewing;
But everything there is exact to my wishes;
For where they don't eat there's no washing of dishes.
I'll be where loud anthems will always be ringing,
But, having no voice, I'll be clear of the singing.
Don't mourn for me now; don't mourn for me never—
I'm going to do nothing for ever and ever."

THE UNICORN
IN THE GARDEN

by James Thurber   3

Note: "booby-hatch" = lunatic asylum.

Once upon a sunny morning a man who sat in a breakfast nook looked up from his scrambled eggs to see a white unicorn with a gold horn quietly cropping the roses in the garden. The man went up to the bedroom where his wife was still asleep and woke her. "There's a unicorn in the garden," he said. "Eating roses." She opened one unfriendly eye and looked at him. "The unicorn is a mythical beast," she said, and turned her back on him. The man walked slowly downstairs and out into the garden. The unicorn was still there; he was now browsing among the tulips. "Here, unicorn," said the man, and he pulled up a lily and gave it to him. The unicorn ate it gravely. With a high heart, because there was a unicorn in his garden, the man went upstairs and roused his wife again. "The unicorn," he said, "ate a lily." His wife sat up in bed and looked at him, coldly. "You are a booby," she said, "and I am going to have you put in the booby-hatch." The man, who had never liked the words "booby" and "booby-hatch," and who liked them even less on a shining morning when there was a unicorn in the garden, thought for a moment. "We'll see about that," he said. He walked over to the door. "He has a golden horn in the middle of his forehead," he told her. Then he went back to the garden to watch the unicorn; but the unicorn had gone away. The man sat down among the roses and went to sleep.

As soon as the husband had gone out of the house, the wife got up and dressed as fast as she could. She was very excited and there was a gloat in her eye. She telephoned the police and she telephoned a psychiatrist; she told them to hurry to her house and bring a strait-jacket. When the police and the psychiatrist arrived they sat down in chairs and looked at her, with great interest. "My husband," she said, "saw a unicorn this morning." The police looked at the psychiatrist and the psychiatrist looked at the police. "He told me it ate a lily," she said. The psychiatrist looked at the police and the police looked at the psychiatrist. "He told me it had a golden horn in the middle of its forehead," she said. At a solemn signal from the psychiatrist, the police leaped from their chairs and seized the wife. They had a hard time subduing her, for she put up a terrific struggle, but they finally subdued her. Just as they got her into the strait-jacket, the husband came back into the house.

"Did you tell your wife you saw a unicorn?" asked the police. "Of course not," said the husband. "The unicorn is a mythical beast." "That's all I wanted to know," said the psychiatrist. "Take her away. I'm sorry, sir, but your wife is as crazy as a jay bird." So they took her away, cursing and screaming, and shut her up in a institution. The husband lived happily ever after.

Moral: Don't count your boobies until they are hatched.

THE PROTHERO FIRE

from "Memories of Christmas"   [3]
by Dylan Thomas

See page 46

EDDICATION

from "Nicholas Nickelby"   4
by Charles Dickens

After some half-hour's delay, Mr. Squeers re-appeared, and the boys took their places and their books, of which latter commodity the average might be about one to eight learners. A few moments having elapsed, during which Mr. Squeers looked very profound, as if he had a perfect apprehension of what was inside all the books, and could say every word of their contents by heart if he only chose to take the trouble, that gentleman called up the first class.

Obedient to this summons there ranged themselves in front of the schoolmaster's desk, half-a-dozen scarecrows, out at knees and elbows, one of whom placed a torn and filthy book beneath his learned eye.

"This is the first class in English spelling and philosophy, Nickleby," said Squeers, beckoning Nicholas to stand beside him, "We'll get up a Latin one, and hand that over to you. Now, then, where's the first boy?"

"Please, sir, he's cleaning the back parlour window," said the temporary head of the philosophical class.

"So he is, to be sure," rejoined Squeers. "We go upon the practical mode of teaching, Nickleby; the regular education system. C-l-e-a-n, clean, verb active, to make bright, to scour. W-i-n, win, d-e-r, der winder, a casement. When the boy knows this out of the book, he goes and does it. [It's just the same principle as the use of the globes.] Where's the second boy?"

"Please, sir, he's weeding the garden," replied a small voice. "To be sure," said Squeers, by no means disconcerted. "So he is. B-o-t, bot, t-i-n, tin, bottin n-e-y, bottinney, noun substantive, a knowledge of plants. When he has learned that bottinney means a knowledge of plants he goes and knows 'em. That's our system, Nickleby; what do you think of it?"

"It's a very useful one, at any rate," answered Nicholas.

"I believe you," rejoined Squeers, [not remarking the emphasis of his usher.] "Third boy, what's a horse?"

"A beast, sir," replied the boy.

"So it is," said Squeers. "Ain't it Nickleby?"

"I believe there is no doubt of that, sir," answered Nicholas.

"Of course there isn't," said Squeers. "A horse is a quadruped, and quadruped's Latin for beast, as everybody that's gone though the grammar knows, or else where's the use of having grammars at all?"

"Where, indeed!" said Nicholas abstractedly.

"As you're perfect in that," resumed Squeers, turning to the boy, "go and look after my horse, and rub him down well, or I'll rub you down. The rest of the class go and draw water up, till somebody tells you to leave off, for it's washing-day to-morrow and they want the coppers [=*wash tubs*] filled."

So saying, he dismissed the first class to their experiments in practical philosophy, and eyed Nicholas with a look, half cunning and half doubtful, as if he were not altogether certain what he might think of him by this time.

THE CONJURER'S REVENGE

by Stephen Leacock   4½

"Now, ladies and gentlemen," said the conjurer, "having shown you that the cloth is absolutely empty, I will proceed to take from it a bowl of goldfish. Presto!"

All around the hall people were saying, "Oh, how wonderful! How does he do it?"

But the Quick Man on the front seat said in a big whisper to the people near him, "He—had—it—up—his—sleeve."

Then the people nodded brightly at the Quick Man and said, "Oh, of course", and everybody whispered round the hall, "He—had—it—up—his—sleeve."

"My next trick," said the conjurer, "is the famous Hindostanee rings. You will notice that the rings are apparently separate; at a blow they all join (clang, clang, clang)— Presto!"

There was a general buzz of stupefaction till the Quick Man was heard to whisper, "He—must—have—had—another—lot—up—his— sleeve."

Again everybody nodded and whispered. "The—rings—were—up—his— sleeve."

The brow of the conjurer was clouded with a gathering frown.

"I will now," he continued, "show you a most amusing trick by which I am enabled to take any number of eggs from a hat. Will some gentleman kindly lend me his hat? Ah, thank you — Presto!"

He extracted seventeen eggs, and for thirty-five seconds the audience began to think that he was wonderful. Then the Quick Man whispered along the front bench, "He–has–a–hen–up–his–sleeve," and all the people whispered it on. "He–has–a–lot–of–hens–up–his–sleeve."

The egg trick was ruined.

It went on like that all through. It transpired from the whispers of the Quick Man that the conjurer must have concealed up his sleeve, in addition to the rings, hens, and fish, several packs of cards, a loaf of bread, a doll's cradle, a live guinea-pig, a fifty-cent piece, and a rocking-chair.

The reputation of the conjurer was rapidly sinking below zero. At the close of the evening he rallied for a final effort.

"Ladies and gentlemen," he said, "I will present to you, in conclusion, the famous Japanese trick recently invented by the natives of Tipperary. Will you, sir," he continued, turning toward the Quick Man, "will you kindly hand me your gold watch?"

It was passed to him.

"Have I your permission to put it into this mortar and pound it to pieces?" he asked savagely.

The Quick Man nodded and smiled.

The conjurer threw the watch into the mortar and grasped a sledge hammer from the table. There was a sound of violent smashing, "He's –slipped–it–up–his–sleeve," whispered the Quick Man.

"Now, sir," continued the conjurer, "will you allow me to take your handkerchief and punch holes in it? Thank you. You see, ladies and gentlemen, there is no deception; the holes are visible to the eye."

The face of the Quick Man beamed. This time the real mystery of the thing fascinated him.

"And now, sir, will you kindly pass me your silk hat and allow me to dance on it? Thank you."

The conjurer made a few rapid passes with his feet and exhibited the hat crushed beyond recognition.

"And will you now, sir, take off your celluloid collar and permit me to burn it in the candle? Thank you, sir. And will you allow me to smash your spectacles for you with my hammer? Thank you."

By this time the features of the Quick Man were assuming a puzzled expression. "This thing beats me," he whispered, "I don't see through it a bit."

There was a great hush upon the audience. Then the conjurer drew himself up to his full height and, with a withering look at the Quick Man, he concluded:

"Ladies and gentlemen, you will observe that I have, with this gentleman's permission, broken his watch, burnt his collar, smashed his spectacles, and danced on his hat. If he will give me the further permission to paint green stripes on his overcoat, or to tie his suspenders in a knot, I shall be delighted to entertain you. If not, the performance is at an end."

And amid a glorious burst of music from the orchestra the curtain fell, and the audience dispersed, convinced that there are some tricks, at any rate, that are not done up the conjurer's sleeve.

from
THE HUNTING OF THE SNARK
by Lewis Carroll   6

" *Just the place for a Snark!" the Bellman cried,*
   As he landed his crew with care;
Supporting each man on the top of the tide
   By a finger entwined in his hair.

"Just the place for a Snark! I have said it twice:
   That alone should encourage the crew.
Just the place for a Snark! I have said it thrice:
   What I tell you three times is true."

The crew was complete: it included a Boots—
   A maker of Bonnets and Hoods—
A Barrister, brought to arrange their disputes—
   And a Broker to value their goods.

A Billiard-maker, whose skill was immense,
    Might perhaps have won more than his share –
But a Banker, engaged at enormous expense,
    Had the whole of their cash in his care.

There was also a Beaver, that paced on the deck,
    Or would sit making lace in the bow:
And had often (the Bellman said) saved them from wreck,
    Though none of the sailors knew how.

There was one who was famed for the number of things
    He forgot when he entered the ship:
His umbrella, his watch, all his jewels and rings,
    And the clothes he had brought for the trip.

He had forty-two boxes, all carefully packed,
    With his name painted clearly on each:
But since he omitted to mention the fact,
    They were all left behind on the beach.

The loss of his clothes hardly mattered because
    He had seven coats on when he came,
With three pair of boots—but the worst of it was,
    He had wholly forgotten his name.

He would answer to "Hi!" or to any loud cry,
    Such as "Fry me!" or "Fritter my wig!"
To "What-you-may-call-um!" or "What-was-his-name!"
    But especially "Thing-um-a-jig!"

While, for those who preferred a more forcible word,
    He had different names from these:
His intimate friends called him "Candle-ends,"
    And his enemies "Toasted-cheese."

"His form is ungainly—his intellect small—"
    So the Bellman would often remark,
"But his courage is perfect! And that, after all,
    Is the thing that one needs with a Snark."

The Bellman himself they all praised to the skies—
  Such a carriage, such ease and such grace!
Such solemnity, too! One could see he was wise,
  The moment one looked in his face!

He had bought a large map representing the sea,
  Without the least vestige of land:
And the crew were much pleased when they found it to be
  A map they could all understand.

"What's the good of Mercator's North Poles and Equators,
  Tropics, Zones, and Meridian Lines?"
So the Bellman would cry: and the crew made reply
  "They are merely conventional signs!

"Other maps are such shapes, with their islands and capes!
  But we've got our brave Captain to thank"
(So the crew would protest) "that he's bought us the best—
  A perfect and absolute blank!"

This was charming no doubt: but they shortly found out
  That the Captain they trusted so well
Had only one notion for crossing the ocean,
  And that was to tingle his bell.

He was thoughtful and grave—but the orders he gave
  Were enough to bewilder a crew.
When he cried "Steer to starboard, but keep her head larboard!"
  What on earth was the helmsman to do?

Then the bowsprit got mixed with the rudder sometimes:
  A thing, as the Bellman remarked,
That frequently happens in tropical climes,
  When a vessel is, so to speak, "snarked."

But the principal failing occurred in the sailing,
  And the Bellman, perplexed and distressed,
Said he had hoped, at least, when the wind blew due East
  That the ship would not travel due West!

After they have landed, the Baker tells a worrying tale:

"My father and mother were honest, though poor—"
  "Skip all that!" cried the Bellman in haste.
"If it once becomes dark, there's no chance of a Snark—
  We have hardly a minute to waste!"

"I skip forty years," said the Baker, in tears,
  "And proceed without further remark
To the day when you took me aboard of your ship
  To help you in hunting the Snark.

"A dear uncle of mine (after whom I was named)
  Remarked, when I bade him farewell—"
"Oh, skip your dear uncle!" the Bellman exclaimed,
  As he angrily tingled his bell.

"He remarked to me then," said that mildest of men,
  " 'If your Snark be a Snark, that is right:
Fetch it home by all means—you may serve it with greens,
  And it's handy for striking a light.

" 'But oh, beamish nephew, beware of the day,
  If your Snark be a Boojum! For then
You will softly and suddenly vanish away,
  And never be met with again!' "

They sought it with thimbles, they sought it with care;
  They pursued it with forks and hope;
They threatened its life with a railway-share;
  They charmed it with smiles and soap.

They shuddered to think that the chase might fail,
  And the Beaver, excited at last,
Went bounding along on the tip of its tail,
  For the daylight was nearly past.

"There is Thingumbob shouting!" the Bellman said.
  "He is shouting like mad, only hark!
He is waving his hands, he is wagging his head,
  He has certainly found a Snark!"

They gazed in delight, while the Butcher exclaimed
  "He was always a desperate wag!"
They beheld him—their Baker—their hero unnamed—
  On the top of a neighbouring crag,

Erect and sublime, for one moment of time.
  In the next, that wild figure they saw
(As if stung by a spasm) plunge into a chasm,
  While they waited and listened in awe.

"It's a Snark!" was the sound that first came to their ears,
  And seemed almost too good to be true.
Then followed a torrent of laughter and cheers:
  Then the ominous words "Its a Boo—"

Then, silence. Some fancied they heard in the air
  A weary and wandering sigh
That sounded like "—jum!" but the others declare
  It was only a breeze that went by.

They hunted till darkness came on, but they found
  Not a button, or feather, or mark,
By which they could tell that they stood on the ground
  Where the Baker had met with the Snark.

In the midst of the word he was trying to say
  In the midst of the laughter and glee,
He had softly and suddenly vanished away—
  For the Snark was a Boojum, you see.

THE CHEESECAKE CHORE

by Paul Jennings 6½
[5]

If you use the cuts suggested, the following may serve as a preliminary explanation.

[Paul Jennings is intrigued by a theory that the Things of this world are combining to work against mankind. 'Thing-areas' are therefore the places where resistance is already almost pointless.]

[According to the Resistentialist philosophy of Pierre-Marie Ventre (*'les choses sont contre nous'*) the 'total' logical course for man is to accept the hostility of the physical world: not to diffuse his energies in open combat in activity in areas where the World-Thing (*dernière chose*, the Ultimate Thing) is explicitly against him, but to search, as unobtrusively as possible, for areas where the World-Thing-Process (Ventre's term) has not yet evolved to 'total thingness' —i.e., where some illusory freedom for man is still possible.

Yet such is man's dual nature that he sometimes fights on in these hopeless 'Thing-areas' — indeed, some Resistentialists see in this a kind of perverse and irrational glory.]

Blackcurrants are in a Thing-area for me. The World-Thing-Process has evolved to consciousness of my desire to grow blackcurrants. It employs special birds with steel beaks that can bite wire. Like commandos, they make breaches in my fruit cage, through which the infantry then pour. I say infantry because they do indeed come on foot; in fact they waddle, they climb heavily up the bushes. They can't fly, they're too full of blackcurrants.

Or the World-Thing, with its infinite resources in chaos and destruction of form, may take the currants away even before the birds can eat them. One year it invented a joke disease called Big Bud. *Big Bud is watching you, Jennings,* it said, and presently brussels sprouts, or so they seemed, began to appear on the bushes, in March.

Nevertheless (O, the glory of man!) this year I got *two pounds* of blackcurrants (there are 537,590 blackcurrants in two pounds. They go down). I mended the wire, I made an awful semi-man of cushions, called Little Bud, and put him in the fruit cage. I walked in it carrying a bored cat (called William Byrd; he couldn't care less, he only eats partridges and toast).

B

There would be strange confrontations in the cage; myself, Little Bud, these birds flapping heavily against the wire (I couldn't even throw anything at them because of all the foliage). They were too drunk to find the holes where they had come in. I stared at them, they stared at me. Little Bud stared at all of us, he seemed to be on their side. In the end I simply held the door open, like an attendant, and they lurched out.

All the same, on a hot day I picked these two pounds. [There is something about currants, in summer; a madness, they're halfway to grapes. I have always remembered that old man in the film *The Grapes of Wrath* who wanted to rub the grapes over his face, to squash the juice out, in the sun, to *be* the grapes. Somewhere there are dusky dances, cymbals, sweat, thirst-madness, bloody juice, communion in a blazing noonday . . .] and the next day, getting this great bowl of two pounds of blackcurrants out of the refrigerator, I knocked a saucer of grated cheese off a higher shelf, or rather the cheese *dived* on to the blackcurrants. I had a bowl of blackcurrants and cheese.

I had come too far by now to give up these blackcurrants, MY blackcurrants, to the World-Thing-Process. I had a confused idea that science would help [(according to Ventre science is a supreme Resistentialist irony; man deludes himself into thinking he controls Things, whereas Things – the motor-car, the aeroplane, and now the Bomb – more and more control him).]

I remembered those experiments where you rubbed glass rods with – heavens, what was it, some special stuff, fur, leather, cottonwool? – and they acquired an electrostatic charge, they attracted bits of paper (or were they *amber* rods; 'electricity' comes from the Greek *Electron*, amber, how odd. Where do you get amber rods?). Perhaps I could make a sort of cheese-magnet. I experimented with a glass rod (thermometer), a plastic rod (perch from toy birdcage), a steel rod (knitting needle), a wooden rod (spoon), rubbed furiously with every kind of textile. I can state categorically that *nothing* attracts cheese.

Then I thought, surely cheese and blackcurrants would have different specific gravities, or differential mass, or whatever the fool thing is called. I added water to the bowl, somehow expecting the blackcurrants to float and the cheese to sink (then I would do something crafty with muslin). Actually the cheese rose, it whirled about in a kind of cheese snowstorm until the tap stopped, then it all settled down and got right in among the lower blackcurrants as well, instead of just lying on the top; and now it was *bonded* to the currants with water.

Also there now seemed to be more cheese, and less blackcurrants. (Cheese does do this. You can *create* cheese in a grater, more comes out than you put in; once thus encouraged, it begins to grow.) And suppose some of the cheese dissolved in the water, encapsulating each currant in a film of cheese? There would be no hope then.

In the end, of course, I had to wash each blackcurrant separately (although they now occupied less space the two pounds now contained 637,948 blackcurrants); an operation best performed by a three-handed man – one hand dipping palmsful of cheesy blackcurrants into a bowl of water, the second picking out individual blackcurrants, the thumb and finger of the third taking off the cheese. But surely, it might be asked, it would be easier simply to hold each palmful under the tap.

Not with us it wouldn't. If we run the tap like that for long we have to start *rodding out drains.*[I'm afraid Ventre is right.]

THE JACKDAW OF RHEIMS

(An Ingoldsby Legend) 6½
by R. H. Barham

The Jackdaw sat on the Cardinal's chair!
Bishop, and abbot, and prior were there;
   Many a monk and many a friar,
   Many a knight and many a squire,
With a great many more of lesser degree,–
In sooth a goodly company;
And they served the Lord Primate on bended knee.
   Never, I ween,
   Was a prouder seen,
Read of in books, or dreamt of in dreams,
Than the Cardinal Lord Archbishop of Rheims!

In and out
Through the motley rout,
That little Jackdaw kept hopping about;
Here and there
Like a dog in a fair,
Over comfits and cates,
And dishes and plates,
Cowl and cope, and rochet and pall,
Mitre and crosier! he hopped upon all!
With saucy air,
He perched on the chair
Where, in state, the great Lord Cardinal sat
In the great Lord Cardinal's great red hat;
And he peered in the face
Of his Lordship's Grace,
With a satisfied look, as if he would say,
"We two are the greatest folks here to-day!"
And the priests with awe,
As such freaks they saw,
Said, "The Devil must be in that little Jackdaw!"

The feast was over, the board was cleared,
The flawns and the custards had all disappeared,
And six little Singing-boys,—dear little souls!
In nice clean faces, and nice white stoles,
Came in order due,
Two by two,
Marching that great refectory through!
A nice little boy had a golden ewer,
Embossed and filled with water, as pure
As any that flows between Rheims and Namur,
Which a nice little boy stood ready to catch
In a fine golden hand-basin made to match.
Two nice little boys, rather more grown,
Carried lavender-water, and eau de Cologne;
And a nice little boy had a nice cake of soap,
Worthy of washing the hands of the Pope.
One little boy more

A napkin bore,
Of the best white diaper, fringed with pink,
And a Cardinal's Hat marked in 'permanent ink'.

The great Lord Cardinal turns at the sight
Of these nice little boys dressed all in white:
From his finger he draws
His costly turquoise;
And, not thinking at all about little Jackdaws,
Deposits it straight
By the side of the plate,
While the nice little boys on his Eminence wait;
Till, when nobody's dreaming of any such thing,
That little Jackdaw hops off with the ring!

There's a cry and a shout,
And a deuce of a rout,
And nobody seems to know what they're about,
But the Monks have their pockets all turned inside out.
The Friars are kneeling,
And hunting and feeling
The carpet, the floor, and the walls, and the ceiling.
The Cardinal drew
Off each plum-coloured shoe,
And left his red stockings exposed to the view;
He peeps, and he feels
In the toes and the heels;
They turn up the dishes,—they turn up the plates,—
They take up the poker and poke out the grates,
They turn up the rugs,
They examine the mugs:—
But, no!—no such thing;—
They can't find The Ring!
And the Abbot declared that, "when nobody twigged it,
Some rascal or other had popped in, and prigged it!"

The Cardinal rose with a dignified look,
He called for his candle, his bell and his book!

In holy anger, and pious grief
He solemnly cursed that rascally thief!
He cursed him at board, he cursed him in bed;
From the sole of his foot to the crown of his head;
He cursed him in sleeping, that every night
He should dream of the devil, and wake in a fright;
He cursed him in eating, he cursed him in drinking,
He cursed him in coughing, in sneezing, in winking;
He cursed him in sitting, in standing, in lying;
He cursed him in walking, in riding, in flying,
He cursed him in living, he cursed him in dying!—
Never was heard such a terrible curse!!
    But what gave rise
    To no little surprise,
Nobody seemed one penny the worse!

    The day was gone,
    The night came on,
The Monks and the Friars they searched till dawn;
    When the Sacristan saw,
    On crumpled claw,
Come limping a poor little lame Jackdaw!
    No longer gay,
    As on yesterday;
His feathers all seemed to be turned the wrong way;—
His pinions drooped—he could hardly stand,—
His head was as bald as the palm of your hand;
    His eye so dim,
    So wasted each limb,
That, heedless of grammar, they all cried, "That's him—
That's the scamp that has done this scandalous thing!
That's the thief that has got my Lord Cardinal's Ring!"
    The poor little Jackdaw,
    When the Monks he saw,
Feebly gave vent to the ghost of a caw;
And turned his bald head, as much as to say,
"Pray, be so good as to walk this way!"
    Slower and slower

> *He limped on before,*
> *Till they came to the back of the belfry door,*
> *Where the first thing they saw,*
> *Midst the sticks and the straw,*
> *Was the* Ring *in the nest of that little Jackdaw!*

> *Then the great Lord Cardinal called for his book,*
> *And off that terrible curse he took;*
> *The mute expression*
> *Served in lieu of confession,*
> *And, being thus coupled with full restitution,*
> *The Jackdaw got plenary absolution!*
> *—When these words were heard,*
> *That poor little bird*
> *Was so changed in a moment, 'twas really absurd.*

> *He grew sleek, and fat;*
> *In addition to that,*
> *A fresh crop of feathers came thick as a mat!*
> *His tail wagged more*
> *Even than before,*
> *But no longer it wagged with an impudent air,*
> *No longer he perched on the Cardinal's chair.*
> *He hopped now about*
> *With a gait devout;*
> *At Matins, at Vespers, he never was out;*
> *And, so far from any more pilfering deeds,*
> *He always seemed telling the Confessor's beads.*
> *If any one lied,—or if anyone swore,—*
> *Or slumbered in prayer-time and happened to snore,*
> *That good Jackdaw*
> *Would give a great 'Caw!'*
> *As much as to say, "Don't do so any more!"*
> *While many remarked, as his manners they saw,*
> *That they "never had known such a pious Jackdaw."*
> *He long lived the pride*
> *Of that country side,*
> *And at last in the odour of sanctity died;*

> *When, as words were too faint*
> *His merits to paint,*
> *The Conclave determined to make him a Saint;*
> *And on newly-made Saints and Popes, as you know,*
> *It's the custom, at Rome, new names to bestow,*
> *So they canonized him by the name of Jim Crow!*

CAPTAIN MURDERER

from "The Uncommercial Traveller"   7½
by Charles Dickens

An horrific tale told to the young Dickens by his nurse.

The first diabolical character who intruded himself on my peaceful youth was a certain Captain Murderer. This wretch must have been an offshoot of the Blue Beard family, but I had no suspicion of the consanguinity [=*relationship*] in those times. His warning name would seem to have awakened no general prejudice against him, for he was admitted into the best society and possessed immense wealth. Captain Murderer's mission was matrimony, and the gratification of a cannibal appetite with tender brides. On his marriage morning, he always caused both sides of the way to church to be planted with curious flowers. and when his bride said, "Dear Captain Murderer, I never saw flowers like these before: what are they called?" he answered, "They are called Garnish for house-lamb," and laughed at his ferocious practical joke in a horrid manner, disquieting the minds of the noble bridal company, with a very sharp show of teeth, then displayed for the first time. He made love in a coach and six, and married in a coach and twelve, and all his horses were milk-white horses with one red spot on the back which he caused to be hidden by the harness. For, the spot *would* come there, though every horse was milk-white when Captain Murderer bought him. And the spot was young bride's blood, (To this terrific point I am indebted for my first personal experience of a shudder and cold beads on the forehead.) When Captain Murderer had made an end of feasting and revelry, and had dismissed the noble guests, and was alone with his wife on the day month after their marriage, it was his whimsical custom to produce a golden rolling-pin and a silver pie-board. Now, there was this special feature in the Captain's courtships, that he always asked if the young lady could make pie-crust; and if she couldn't by nature or education, she was taught. Well. When the bride saw Captain Murderer produce the golden rolling-pin and silver pie-board, she remembered this, and turned up her laced-silk sleeves to make a pie. The Captain brought out a silver pie-dish of immense capacity, and the Captain brought out flour and butter and eggs and all things needful, except the inside of the pie; of materials for the staple of the pie itself, the Captain brought out none. Then said the lovely bride, "Dear Captain Murderer, what pie is this to be?" He replied, "A meat pie." Then said the lovely bride, "Dear Captain Murderer, I see no meat." The Captain humorously retorted, "Look in the glass." She looked in the glass, but still she saw no meat, and then the Captain roared with laughter, and suddenly frowning and drawing his sword, bade her roll out the crust. So she rolled out the crust, dropping large tears upon it all the time because he was so cross, and when she had lined the dish with crust and had cut the crust all ready to fit the top, the Captain called out, "*I* see the meat in the glass!" And the bride looked up at the glass, just in time to see the Captain cutting her head off; and he chopped her in pieces, and peppered her, and salted her, and put her in the pie, and sent it to the baker's and ate it all, and picked the bones.

Captain Murderer went on in this way, prospering exceedingly, until he came to choose a bride from two twin sisters, and at first didn't know which to choose. For, though one was fair and the other dark, they were both equally beautiful. But the fair twin loved him, and the dark twin hated him, so he chose the fair one. The dark twin would have prevented the marriage if she could, but she couldn't; however, on the night before it, much suspecting Captain Murderer, she stole out and climbed his garden wall, and looked in at his window through a chink in the shutter, and saw him having his teeth filed sharp. Next day she listened all day, and heard him make his joke about the house-lamb. And that day month, he had the paste rolled out, and cut the fair twin's head off, and chopped her in pieces, and peppered her, and salted her, and put her in the pie, and sent it to the baker's, and ate it all, and picked the bones.

Now, the dark twin had had her suspicions much increased by the filing of the Captain's teeth, and again by the house-lamb joke. Putting all things together when he gave out that her sister was dead, she divined the truth, and determined to be revenged. So, she went up to Captain Murderer's house, and knocked at the knocker and pulled at the bell, and when the Captain came to the door, said: "Dear Captain Murderer, marry me next, for I always loved you and was jealous of my sister." The Captain took it as a compliment, and made a polite answer, and the marriage was quickly arranged. On the night before it, the bride again climbed to his window, and again saw him having his teeth filed sharp. At this sight she laughed such a terrible laugh at the chink in the shutter, that the Captain's blood curdled, and he said: "I hope nothing has disagreed with me!" At that, she laughed again, a still more terrible laugh, and the shutter was opened and search made, but she was nimbly gone, and there was no one. Next day they went to church in a coach and twelve, and were married. And that day month, she rolled the pie-crust out, and Captain Murderer cut her head off, and chopped her in pieces, and peppered her, and salted her, and put her in the pie, and sent it to the baker's, and ate it all, and picked the bones.

But before she began to roll out the paste she had taken a deadly poison of a most awful character, distilled from toads's eyes and spiders' knees; and Captain Murderer had hardly picked her last bone, when he began to swell, and to turn blue, and to be all over spots, and to scream. And he went on swelling and turning bluer; and being more all over spots and screaming, until he reached from floor to ceiling and from wall to wall; and then at one o'clock in the morning, he blew up with a loud explosion. At the sound of it, all the milk-white horses in the stables broke their halters and went mad, and then they galloped over everybody in Captain Murderer's house (beginning with the family blacksmith who had filed his teeth) until the whole were dead, and then they galloped away.

KING PELLINORE'S JOUST

from "The Sword in the Stone"   [8]
by T. H. White

See page 87

UB
by Paul Jennings 8

A few weeks ago there was an item of news about a man in America who was arrested for continually running into shiny new cars with his jalopy (this excellent word, pronounced to rhyme with, but not associated with "sloppy", is the American expression for an old car). When asked for an explanation he replied simply "I just don't like 'em."

How I agree with that man! I should like to take him out in UB. UB is the name of my car, which is not only a jalopy but has these fascinating letters in its registration. UB is pronounced to rhyme and is sometimes associated with "pub". It is inconceivable that my car should be called AD, or BO, or MO, let alone anything Polish or Czechoslovakian like KX or ZB. It is as much UB as a mangle is a mangle.

I bought it before the war for £7 from a clerkly sort of man who had bought it brand-new in 1928. He could hardly have gone out much in it, because he had spent every week-end doing the weekly tasks laid down in the instruction book. It was almost the same as on the day it rolled off the assembly line, when this now grey-haired man was a conveyancer, or perhaps an assayer.

On second thoughts I am pretty sure it didn't come off an assembly line at all. Cars like UB were made lovingly, one at a time, by elderly, shirt-sleeved craftsmen such as one used to see in the drawings of Mr Heath Robinson — men who only twenty years previously had been building gigs, traps and phaetons. One can tell this from the position of the headlights, which are at the side of the windscreen. People who do not understand about UB ask me sarcastically where I get the acetylene these days, but that is only because they are peeved at not being able to find the battery, which is under the passenger's seat. I always see UB taking shape in a place which I visualise as a converted barn still filled with a faint smell of musty hay. Dust floats in the sunbeams filtering through a small, high window. The craftsmen are in consultation.

"Gideon," says one of them, "let us have an oil-gauge in this one."

His mate looks perturbed. "You know what we said about not buying anything outside, Eli," he says.

"Nay, Gideon, it is a thing we can make ourselves. I thought of it as I was coming through Barton's Copse this morning. Lookee here." And he goes on to explain UB's oil-gauge.

It is for this alone that I would rather have UB than my friend Harblow's car, in which the dashboard is a mass of instruments. For my oil-gauge is not an instrument at all. It is a button. You start the engine and press this button in. If it comes out again you know the oil pressure is all right. Either it is all right or it isn't. There is none of this worrying about falling below a certain pressure (and I suspect that most people, like Harblow, don't know what this pressure is supposed to be, anyway).

It is the same with the rest of the car. Harblow would never, in his most boastful moments, say he really understands his carburettor, which has about five pipes going into it and also has an absurd frying-pan thing full of *oil* on the top, which he says lamely is an *air-cleaner*. UB has been bumbling along now for twenty years with the good old British atmosphere, which is clean enough for us. And whoever heard of cleaning air, or anything else for that matter, with *oil*? Gideon, Eli and Co. knew better. They knew that a carburettor is essentially a thing with holes in it for mixing petrol and air in a fine spray ready for explosion, and they didn't go messing about with things full of oil, which would obviously find its way eventually to these holes and block them up, in much the same way as marmalade always finds its way between one's fingers. And there is one pipe going into my carburettor. You know where you are.

Harblow's car has the petrol tank at the back. It is connected to the engine, which is much higher up and about ten feet away, by a complicated system of pipes and taps and pumps and filters (there seems to be a mania for filtering and cleaning in modern cars). Any one of these things can go wrong, and usually does, about twelve miles from Swindon on a dark wet night. Whenever I am with him it is a thing called the automatic pump. We can't even begin to repair it until the engine has cooled down because it is right in the bowels of the mechanism and one burns one's knuckles against the hot cylinder block. This pump seems to have about a hundred washers, which either get dropped and lost or are discovered to have been left out when the whole thing has been tightened up again. After half an hour's sucking, blowing and cursing Harblow produces a little wire gauze thing full of the most amazing geological specimens. "The filter is choked," he says indignantly.

"This petrol is a scandal." Well, I buy the same petrol and it doesn't choke my filter because there isn't one. I have a theory that a strange chemical action takes place in these filters and that the petrol crystallises out. Gideon and Eli didn't have to worry about pumps, automatic or otherwise, because UB's petrol tank is behind the dashboard and the stuff just *falls* down according to the well-known laws of Isaac Newton.

Then there are the brakes. Every three months or so Harblow notices a funny smell and he gets out and finds that his rear brake linings are practically on fire. He has hydraulic brakes (*more* pipes and, I shouldn't be surprised, more filters) and to put them right it is necessary to perform a terrible operation called bleeding the master cylinder. UB's brakes, although a considerable advance in their day on the earlier models of Gideon and Eli, which probably had a stout oak block against the wheel rim operated by iron levers, are simplicity itself. They are operated by wire cables which pass over a little wheel coming down on a screw thing from the floor of the car. If the brakes are too tight you screw the wheel down a bit. It takes one minute. Bleeding the master cylinder takes Harblow three week-ends at home and then two months in a garage.

Another thing of which people like Harblow seem to be inordinately proud is the fact that their engines are mounted on rubber. It is true that when he starts up his car during his eternal attentions to the innumerable cleaners, boosters, dust-baths, bird-bins and fly-traps the whole engine does jump about in a most insecure-looking fashion, so that you can see about ten of it. But it seems very precious to me. UB's engine is bolted firmly to the chassis, and when it is ticking over it is the mudguards of which you see about ten; there is a nice comfortable thubbing feeling as you get into the seat. Rubber is perishable, and this is one of the many reasons why you often see cars like Harblow's on scrap heaps but never cars like UB. It is because the owners have got tired of bleeding the master cylinder and adjusting the oil-filter, the petrol-filter and the air-filter and buying new blocks of rubber . You couldn't have left one of these rubber-mounted cars at the bottom of the garden throughout the whole war, as I did UB, and found it ready to drive again after fitting a new hood, new plugs, new windscreen-wiper (and, come to think of it, a new windscreen), two new tyres, new king-pins, new front spring, new cylinder head, new battery, re-wiring and re-painting, drying out the magneto in the oven, getting the dynamo re-wound and mending the leaks in the radiator.

You would have found the rubber had perished.

THE MOUSE

by "Saki"   10
                                                                     [9]

Theodoric Voler had been brought up, from infancy to the confines of
middle age, by a fond mother whose chief solicitude had been to keep him
screened from what she called the coarser realities of life. When she died she
left Theodoric alone in a world that was as real as ever, and a good deal
coarser than he considered it had any need to be. To a man of his
temperament and upbringing even a simple railway journey was crammed
with petty annoyances and minor discords, and as he settled himself down in
a second-class compartment one September morning he was conscious of
ruffled feelings and general discompShature. He had been staying at a country
vicarage, [the inmates of which had been certainly neither brutal nor
bacchanalian, but their supervision of the domestic establishment had been of
that lax order which invites disaster.] The pony carriage that was to take him
to the station had never been properly ordered, and when the moment for his
departure drew near the handy-man who should have produced the required
article was nowhere to be found. In this emergency Theodoric, to his mute
but very intense disgust, found himself obliged to collaborate with the vicar's
daughter in the task of harnessing the pony, which necessitated groping about
in an ill-lighted outhouse called a stable, and smelling very like one – except
in patches where it smelt of mice. [Without being actually afraid of mice,
Theodoric classed them among the coarser incidents of life, and considered
that Providence, with a little exercise of moral courage, might long ago have
recognized that they were not indispensable, and have withdrawn them from
circulation.] As the train glided out of the station Theodoric's nervous
imagination accused himself of exhaling [= *giving off*] a weak odour of
stableyard, and possibly of displaying a mouldy straw or two on his usually
well-brushed garments. Fortunately the only other occupant of the
compartment, a lady of about the same age as himself, seemed inclined for
slumber rather than scrutiny; the train was not due to stop till the terminus
was reached, in about an hour's time, and the carriage was of the

old-fashioned sort, that held no communication with a corridor, therefore no further travelling companions were likely to intrude on Theodoric's semi-privacy. And yet the train had scarcely attained its normal speed before he became reluctantly but vividly aware that he was not alone in his own clothes. A warm, creeping movement over his flesh betrayed the unwelcome and highly resented presence, unseen but poignant, of a strayed mouse, that had evidently dashed into its present retreat during the episode of the pony harnessing. Furtive stamps and shakes and wildly directed pinches failed to dislodge the intruder, [whose motto, indeed, seemed to be Excelsior;] and the lawful occupant of the clothes lay back against the cushions and endeavoured rapidly to evolve some means for putting an end to the dual ownership. [It was unthinkable that he should continue for the space of a whole hour in the horrible position of a Rowton House for vagrant mice (already his imagination had at least doubled the numbers of the alien invasion). On the other hand,] nothing less drastic than partial disrobing would ease him of his tormentor, and to undress in the presence of a lady, even for so laudable a purpose, was an idea that made his eartips tingle in a blush of abject shame. He had never been able to bring himself even to the mild exposure of open-work socks in the presence of the fair sex. And yet — the lady in this case was to all appearances soundly and securely asleep; the mouse, on the other hand, seemed to be trying to crowd a Wanderjahr [= *World Tour*] into a few strenuous minutes. [If there is any truth in the theory of transmigration, this particular mouse must certainly have been in a former state a member of the Alpine Club.] Sometimes in its eagerness it lost its footing and slipped for half an inch or so; and then, in fright, or more probably temper, it bit. Theodoric was goaded into the most audacious undertaking of his life. Crimsoning to the hue of a beetroot and keeping an agonized watch on his slumbering fellow-traveller, he swiftly and noiselessly secured the ends of his railway-rug to the racks on either side of the carriage, so that a substantial curtain hung athwart the compartment. In the narrow dressing-room that he had thus improvised he proceeded with violent haste to extricate himself partially and the mouse entirely from the surrounding casings of tweed and half-wool. As the unravelled mouse gave a wild leap to the floor, the rug, slipping its fastening at either end, also came down with a heart-curdling flop, and almost simultaneously the awakened sleeper opened her eyes. With a movement almost quicker than the mouse's, Theodoric pounced on the rug, and hauled its ample folds chin-high over his dismantled person as he collapsed into the further corner of the carriage. The blood raced and beat in the veins of his neck and forehead, while he waited dumbly for the communication-cord to be pulled. The lady, however, contented herself with a silent stare at her strangely muffled companion. How much had she seen, Theodoric queried to himself, and in any case what on earth must she think of his present posture?

"I think I have caught a chill," he ventured desperately.

"Really, I'm sorry," she replied. "I was just going to ask if you would open this window."

"I fancy it's malaria," he added, his teeth chattering slightly, as much from fright as from a desire to support his theory.

"I've got some brandy in my hold-all, if you'll kindly reach it down for me," said his companion.

"Not for worlds — I mean, I never take anything for it," he assured her earnestly.

"I suppose you caught it in the Tropics?"

Theodoric, whose acquaintance with the Tropics was limited to an annual present of a chest of tea from an uncle in Ceylon, felt that even the malaria was slipping from him. Would it be possible, he wondered, to disclose the real state of affairs to her in small instalments?

"Are you afraid of mice?" he ventured, growing, if possible, more scarlet in the face.

"Not unless they came in quantities, [like those that ate up Bishop Hatto.] Why do you ask?"

"I had one crawling inside my clothes just now," said Theodoric in a voice that hardly seemed his own. "It was a most awkward situation."

"It must have been, if you wear your clothes at all tight," she observed; "but mice have strange ideas of comfort."

"I had to get rid of it while you were asleep," he continued; then, with a gulp, he added, "it was getting rid of it that brought me to — to this."

"Surely leaving off one small mouse wouldn't bring on a chill," she exclaimed, with a levity that Theodoric accounted abominable.

Evidently she had detected something of his predicament, and was enjoying his confusion. All the blood in his body seemed to have mobilized in one concentrated blush, and an agony of abasement, worse than a myriad mice, crept up and down over his soul. And then, as reflection began to assert itself, sheer terror took the place of humiliation. With every minute that passed the train was rushing nearer to the crowded and bustling terminus where dozens of prying eyes would be exchanged for the one paralysing pair that watched him from the further corner of the carriage. There was one slender despairing chance, which the next few minutes must decide. His fellow-traveller might relapse into a blessed slumber. But as the minutes throbbed by, that chance ebbed away. The furtive glance with Theodoric stole at her from time to time disclosed only an unwinking wakefulness.

"I think we must be getting near now," she presently observed.

Theodoric had already noted with growing terror the recurring stacks of small, ugly dwellings that heralded the journey's end. The words acted as a signal. Like a hunted beast breaking cover and dashing madly towards some other haven of momentary safety he threw aside his rug, and struggled frantically into his dishevelled garments. He was conscious of dull suburban stations racing past the window, of a choking, hammering sensation in his throat and heart, and of an icy silence in that corner towards which he dared not look. Then as he sank back in his seat, clothed and almost delirious, the train slowed down to a final crawl, and the woman spoke.

"Would you be so kind," she asked, "as to get me a porter to put me into a cab? It's a shame to trouble you when you're feeling unwell, but being blind makes one so helpless at a railway station."

MEMORIES OF CHRISTMAS

by Dylan Thomas

13

[3]

[One Christmas was so much like another, in those years, around the sea-town corner now, and out of all sound except the distant speaking of the voices I sometimes hear a moment before sleep, that I can never remember whether it snowed for six days and six nights when I was twelve or whether it snowed for twelve days and twelve nights when I was six; or whether the ice broke and the skating grocer vanished like a snowman through a white trap-door on that same Christmas Day that the mince-pies finished Uncle Arnold and we tobogganed down the seaward hill, all the afternoon, on the best tea-tray, and Mrs Griffiths complained, and we threw a snowball at her niece, and my hands burned so, with the heat and the cold, when I held them in front of the fire, that I cried for twenty minutes and then had some jelly.

All the Christmases roll down the hill towards the Welsh-speaking sea, like a snowball growing whiter and bigger and rounder, like a cold and headlong moon bundling down the sky that was our street; and they stop at the rim of the ice-edged, fish-freezing waves, and I plunge my hands in the snow and bring out whatever I can find; holly or robins or pudding, squabbles and carols and oranges and tin whistles, and the fire in the front room, and bang go the crackers, and holy, holy, holy, ring the bells, and the glass bells shaking on the tree, and Mother Goose, and Struwelpeter — oh! the baby-burning flames and the clacking scissorman! — Billy Bunter and Black Beauty, Little Women and boys who have three helpings, Alice and Mrs Potter's badgers, penknives, teddy-bears — named after a Mr Theodore Bear, their inventor, or father, who died recently in the United States — mouth-organs, tin-soldiers, and blancmange, and Auntie Bessie playing "Pop Goes the Weasel" and "Nuts in May" and "Oranges and Lemons" on the untuned piano in the parlour all through the thimble-hiding musical-chairing blind-man's-buffing party at the end of the never-to-be-forgotten day at the end of the unremembered year.

In goes my hand into that wool-white bell-tongued ball of holidays resting at the margin of the carol-singing sea, and out come Mrs Prothero and the firemen.]

It was on the afternoon of the day of Christmas Eve, and I was in Mrs Prothero's garden, waiting for cats, with her son Jim. It was snowing. It was always snowing at Christmas; December, in my memory, is white as Lapland, though there were no reindeers. But there were cats. Patient, cold, and callous, our hands wrapped in socks, we waited to snowball the cats. Sleek and long as jaguars and terrible-whiskered, spitting and snarling they would slink and sidle over the white back-garden walls, and the lynx-eyed hunters, Jim and I, fur-capped and moccasined trappers from Hudson's Bay off Eversley Road, would hurl our deadly snowballs at the green of their eyes. The wise cats never appeared. We were so still, Eskimo-footed arctic marksmen in the muffling silence of the eternal snows — eternal, ever since Wednesday — that we never heard Mrs Prothero's first cry from her igloo at the bottom of the garden. Or, if we heard it at all, it was, to us, like the far-off challenge of our enemy and prey, the neighbour's Polar Cat. But soon the voice grew louder. "Fire!" cried Mrs Prothero, and she beat the dinner-gong. And we ran down the garden, with the snowballs in our arms, towards the house, and smoke, indeed, was pouring out of the dining-room, and the gong was bombilating, and Mrs Prothero was announcing ruin like a town-crier in Pompeii. This was better than all the cats in Wales standing on the wall in a row. We bounded into the house, laden with snowballs, and stopped at the open door of the smoke-filled room. Something was burning all right; perhaps it was Mr Prothero, who always slept there after midday dinner with a newspaper over his face; but he was standing in the middle of the room, saying "A fine Christmas!" and smacking at the smoke with a slipper.

"Call the fire-brigade," cried Mrs Prothero as she beat the gong.

"They won't be there," said Mr Prothero, "It's Christmas."

There was no fire to be seen, only clouds of smoke and Mr Prothero standing in the middle of them, waving his slipper as though he were conducting.

"Do something," he said.

And we threw all our snowballs into the smoke — I think we missed Mr Prothero — and ran out of the house to the telephone-box.

"Let's call the police as well," Jim said.

"And the ambulance."

"And Ernie Jenkins, he likes fires."

But we only called the fire-brigade, and soon the fire-engine came and three tall men in helmets brought a hose into the house and Mr Prothero got out just in time before they turned it on. Nobody could have had a noisier Christmas Eve. And when the firemen turned off the hose and were standing in the wet and smoky room, Jim's aunt, Miss Prothero, came downstairs and peered in at them. Jim and I waited, very quietly, to hear what she would say to them. She said the right thing, always. She looked at the three tall firemen in their shining helmets, standing among the smoke and cinders and dissolving snowballs, and she said: "Would you like something to read?"

[Now out that bright white snowball of Christmas gone comes the stocking, the stocking of stockings, that hung at the foot of the bed with the arm of a golliwog dangling over the top and small bells ringing in the toes. There was a company, gallant and scarlet but never nice to taste though I always tried when very young, of belted and busbied and musketed lead soldiers so soon to lose their heads and legs in the wars on the kitchen table after the tea-things, the mince-pies, and the cakes that I helped to make by stoning the raisins and eating them, had been cleared away; and a bag of moist and many-coloured jelly-babies and a folded flag and a false nose and a tram-conductor's cap and a machine that punched tickets and rang a bell;

never a catapult; once, by a mistake that no one could explain, a little hatchet; and a rubber buffalo, or it may have been a horse, with a yellow head and haphazard legs; and a celluloid duck that made, when you pressed it, a most unducklike noise, a mewing moo that an ambitious cat might make who wishes to be a cow; and a painting-book in which I could make the grass, the trees, the sea, and the animals any colour I pleased: and still the dazzling sky-blue sheep are grazing in the red field under a flight of rainbow-beaked and pea-green birds.

Christmas morning was always over before you could say Jack Frost. And look! suddenly the pudding was burning! Bang the gong and call the fire-brigade and the book-loving firemen! Someone found the silver three-penny-bit with a currant on it; and the someone was always Uncle Arnold. The motto in my cracker read:

> *Let's all have fun this Christmas Day,*
> *Let's play and sing and shout hooray!*

and the grown-ups turned their eyes towards the ceiling, and Auntie Bessie, who had already been frightened, by a clockwork mouse, whimpered at the sideboard and had some elderberry wine. And someone put a glass bowl full of nuts on the littered table, and my uncle said, as he said once every year: "I've got a shoe-nut here. Fetch me a shoe-horn to open it, boy."

And dinner was ended.

And I remember that on the afternoon of Christmas Day, when the others sat around the fire and told each other that this was nothing, no, nothing, to the great snowbound and turkey-proud yule-log-crackling holly-berry-bedizined and kissing-under-the- mistletoe Christmas when *they* were children, I would go out, school-capped and gloved and mufflered, with my bright new boots squeaking, into the white world on to the seaward hill, to call on Jim and Dan and Jack and to walk with them through the silent snowscape of our town.

We went padding through the streets, leaving huge deep footprints in the snow, on the hidden pavements.

"I bet people'll think there's been hippoes."

"What would you do if you saw a hippo coming down Terrace Road?"

"I'd go like this, bang! I'd throw him over the railings and roll him down the hill and then I'd tickle him under the ear and he'd wag his tail . . ."

"What would you do if you saw *two* hippoes . . .?"

Iron-flanked and bellowing he-hippoes clanked and blundered and battered

through the scudding snow towards us as we passed by Mr Daniel's house.
"Let's post Mr Daniel a snowball through his letterbox."
"Let's write things in the snow."
"Let's write 'Mr Daniel looks like a spaniel' all over his lawn."
"Look," Jack said, "I'm eating snow-pie."
"What's it taste like?"
"Like snow-pie," Jack said.
Or we walked on the white shore.
"Can the fishes see it's snowing?"
"They think it's the sky falling down."
The silent one-clouded heavens drifted on to the sea.
"All the old dogs have gone."
Dogs of a hundred mingled makes yapped in the summer at the sea-rim
and yelped at the trespassing mountains of the waves.
"I bet St Bernards would like it now."
And we were snowblind travellers lost on the north hills, and the
great dewlapped dogs, with brandy-flasks round their necks, ambled and
shambled up to us, baying "Excelsior."
We returned home through the desolate poor sea-facing streets where only
a few children fumbled with bare red fingers in the thick wheel-rutted snow
and cat-called after us, their voices fading away, as we trudged uphill, into the
cries of the dock-birds and the hooters of ships out in the white and whirling
bay.
Bring out the tall tales now that we told by the fire as we roasted
chestnuts and the gaslight bubbled low. Ghosts with their heads under their
arms trailed their chains and said "whooo" like owls in the long nights when I
dared not look over my shoulder; wild beasts lurked in the cubby-hole under
the stairs where the gas-meter ticked. "Once upon a time," Jim said, "there
were three boys, just like us, who got lost in the dark in the snow, near
Bethesda Chapel, and this is what happened to them . . ." It was the most
dreadful happening I had ever heard.
And I remember that we went singing carols once, a night or two before
Christmas Eve, when there wasn't the shaving of a moon to light the secret,
white-flying streets. At the end of a long road was a drive that led to a large
house, and we stumbled up the darkness of the drive that night, each one of
us afraid, each one holding a stone in his hand made through the drive-trees
noises as of old and unpleasant and maybe web-footed men wheezing in
caves. We reached the black bulk of the house.

"What shall we give them?" Dan whispered.

" 'Hark the Herald'? 'Christmas comes but Once a Year'?"

"No," Jack said: "We'll sing 'Good King Wenceslas.' I'll count three."

One, two, three, and we began to sing, our voices high and seemingly distant in the snow-felted darkness round the house that was occupied by nobody we knew. We stood close together, near the dark door.

> *Good King Wenceslas looked out*
> *On the Feast of Stephen.*

And then a small, dry voice, like the voice of someone who has not spoken for a long time, suddenly joined our singing: a small, dry voice from the other side of the door: a small, dry voice through the keyhole. And when we stopped running we were outside *our* house; the front room was lovely and bright; the gramophone was playing; we saw the red and white balloons hanging from the gas-bracket: uncles and aunts sat by the fire: I thought I smelt our supper being fried in the kitchen. Everything was good again, and Christmas shone through all the familiar town.

"Perhaps it was a ghost," Jim said.

"Perhaps it was trolls," Dan said, who was always reading.

"Let's go in and see if there's any jelly left," Jack said. And we did that.]

EBENEEZER THE GOAT

by "Sapper"

13½
[12½]

A story from the trenches of the 1st World War – The Germans are referred to as Boches.

Driver Robert Brown, [as I have already remarked,] was an admirable man in many ways. And I have frequently observed to other members of the mess, that one of the things that most endeared him to me was his love of animals.

Brown was not a beauty, I admit: his face was of the general-utility order, and he had a partiality for singing a dreadful song of which he only knew one

line — at least that is all we ever heard, thank Heaven! At cockcrow, 'neath
the midday sun, at eventide, did he foist upon a long-suffering world, with a
powerful and somewhat flat voice, the following despairing wail: "What a
faice, what a faice, what a norrible faice, lumme, what a faice she 'ad."
Occasional streams of invective [= *cursing*] issued from neighbouring
dug-outs. The result was immaterial; he merely appraised other portions of
the lady's anatomy. Once I remember the cook was ill; Brown did his work.
He was a good lad — he always did everyone else's work. We were hungry —
very hungry — and he, stout fellow, was preparing our repast.

"Homlette, sir," he had murmured confidentially, "peas and taters, and
fresh meat!" and with his honest face shining with eagerness to prepare this
[Epicurean] banquet he had gone about his business. The shadows
lengthened — an appetising smell greeted our nostrils; we forgave him his
untoward references to his adored one's "faice." Then it happened.

"What a neye, what a neye, what a norrible heye, lumme" — there was a
fearful pause and sizzling noise — "lumme, the whole perishing homlette's in
the fire." It was; and in a gallant attempt at rescue he upset the meat in an
adjacent stagnant pool. The only thing we got were the peas, and they rattled
on the tin plates like shrapnel bullets.

However, as I've said several times, he was an admirable lad, and a love of
animals atoned for a multitude of sins. At least everyone thought so, until he
adopted a goat. It was an animal of unprepossessing aspect and powerful smell
— very powerful. [I speak with some authority on the subject of goats, for in
the course of my service I have lived for a space on an abominable island "set in
a sapphire sea." Ninety per cent of its population are goats, the remainder
priests; and without intermission, in a ceaseless stream, the savour of that
island flows upwards and outwards. I therefore claim to speak with authority,
and Brown's goat would have held its own with ease in any community.]

He accommodated it in a special dug-out, from which it habitually
escaped; generally at full speed just as the Major was passing. When the Major
had been knocked down twice, Brown was accorded an interview. It was a
breezy little affair, that interview, and Brown for some hours seen.ed a trifle
dazed. For some time after he was busy in the goat's dug-out, and when I
passed on my way out to a job of work that evening, I found him,
contemplating his handiwork with pride. Not content with doubling its
head-rope, he had shackled the goat fore and aft to pegs in the ground — one
fore-leg and one hind-leg being secured by rope to two pegs firmly driven into
the floor of the dug-out.

"That's done you, my beauty," I heard him murmuring; and then he relapsed into his song, while the goat watched him pensively out of one eye.

I subsequently discovered that it was about three o'clock next morning it happened. The goat, having slipped its collar and pulled both pegs, shot from its dug-out with a goat-like cry of joy. Then the pegs alarmed it, dangling from its legs — and it went mad. At least, that's what the Major said. It appeared that, having conducted an exhaustive survey of a portion of the line with the General and his staff, they had returned to refresh weary nature with a portion of tongue and a bottle of fine old port — the old and bold, full of crustiness. Hardly had they got to it, when, with a dreadful and ear-splitting noise, the goat bounded through the door of the dug-out. One peg flying round caught the General on the knee, the other wrapped itself round the leg of the table. The old gentleman, under the impression that the Germans had broken through, drew his revolver, and with a great cry of "Death rather than dishonour," discharged his weapon six times into the blue. Mercifully there were no casualties, as the staff, with great present of mind, had hurled themselves flat on their faces during this dangerous proceeding. Each shot came to rest in the crate containing the whisky, and the fumes from the liquid which flowed over the floor so excited the goat that with one awful effort it broke loose and disappeared into an adjacent cornfield. [I cannot vouch for all this — in fact the mess as a body received the story coldly. The junior subaltern even went so far as to murmur to another graceless youth that it was one way of accounting for eight bottles of whisky and two of port — and that it was very creditable to all concerned that they said it was a goat, and not a spotted megothaurus. All I can vouch for is that] when the Major woke up the next day, he issued an ultimatum. The goat must go — alive if possible; dead if necessary — but if he ever again saw the accursed beast, he, personally would destroy it with gun-cotton. As he really seemed in earnest about the matter, I decided that something must be done. I sent for Brown.

"Brown," I said when he appeared, "the goat must go."

"What, Hebeneezer, sir?" he answered in dismay.

"I do not know its name," I returned firmly, "and I was under the impression that it was a female; but if you call it Ebeneezer, then Ebeneezer must go." He became pensive. "Dead or alive that accursed mammal must depart, never to return. It has already seriously injured the Major's constitution."

"It has, sir?" There was a world of surprise in his tone. "Of course, it don't do to go playing about with it, or crossing it like, but —"

"The goat has done the crossing. Twice — at full speed."

"'E seems a bit quiet this morning, sir. Off his food like. And 'e's lost a bit of 'is tail." Brown scratched his head meditatively.

The fact did not surprise me — but I preserved a discreet silence. "Get rid of it this morning, and see that it never returns!" I ordered, and the incident closed — at least I thought so at the time.

Brown reported his departure that evening, and with a sigh of relief from the Major the odoriferous Ebeneezer was struck off the strength with effect from that day's date. It is true that I noticed strange and mysterious absences on the part of my servant when he left carrying something in paper and returned empty-handed, and that in the back of my mind I had a vague suspicion that somewhere in the neighbourhood there still remained that evil-smelling animal looked after and fed by Robert Brown. But, as a week passed and we saw and smelt the beast no more, my suspicions were lulled to rest, and I dismissed the untoward incident from my mind. I am always of an optimistic disposition!

I should say it was about ten days after Ebeneezer's departure that I awoke one morning early to the sound of a violent altercation without.

"I tells you, you can't see the Major. 'E's in 'is bath." Peering out, I saw Brown and the cook warding off two extremely excited Belgians.

"Bath! Bath! *Qu'est que c'est* — bath!" The stouter Belgian gesticulated freely. "You are — vot you say — *du génie, n'est-ce-pas?* Eet is important — ver important that I see monsieur le commandant."

"Look here, cully," murmured the cook, removing a clay pipe from his mouth and expectorating [=*spitting*] with great accuracy; "moosoo le commandant is in 'is bath — see. You'll 'ave to wait. Bath — savez. *Eau*." He pointed to a bucket of water.

"*Mon Dieu!*" shuddered the Belgian. "*Eh bien! mon ami,* ees zere anozer officer? It is *très important*." He was getting excited again. "*Les Boches* — zere is a *bruit* under ze earth — *comprenez*? Zey make a — oh! ze word, ze word — zey make *une mine,* and zen we all go Pouff!" He waved his hands to Heaven.

"Mean. Mean," remarked the cook contemplatively. "Wot the deuce does he mean? Anyway, Bob, we might take 'im on as a sparklet machine."

Then I thought it was about time I came to the rescue. "What's all the trouble, Brown?" I asked, coming out of the dug-out.

"These 'ere blokes, sir ..." he began; but as both Belgians began talking at once, he got no further.

"Ah! monsieur," they cried, "*vous êtes du génie?*" I assured them I was of the engineers. "Then come *vite, s'il vous plait.* We are of ze artillery, and ze Germans zey make *une mine, n'est-ce-pas?* We go up Pouff. Our guns zey go up Pouff — *aussi.*"

"Mining," I cried, "the Germans mining here! Impossible, messieurs. Why, we're a mile and half behind the firing-line." I regret to say I was a little peevish.

Nevertheless they assured me it was so — not once, but many times. Strange noises, they affirmed, were heard in the bowels of the earth near their battery — mysterious rumblings occurred; they continually assured me they were going Pouff!

I went to the Major. He was not in a good temper — he rarely is in the early morning — and the last blade of his safety razor was blunt.

"Mining here!" he barked. "What the deuce are they talking about? It's probably nesting time for woodpeckers or something. Oh! yes — go away and see," in reply to my question. "Anything to get those two embryo volcanoes off the premises: and don't let 'em come back, for Heaven's sake!"

So I went, Undoubtedly there were noises — very strange subterranean noises, in front of that battery. Moreover, the sounds seemed to come from different places. At times they were very loud; at others they ceased. The excitement soon became intense. Stout officers lay all over the ground with their ears pressed in the mud. The commandant of the battery ran round in small circles saying Pouff! distractedly. In fact everyone said Pouff! to everyone else. It became the password of the morning. Then at last the crucial moment arrived. The centre of the storm, so to speak, had been located — the place where, so far as we could tell, the noise seemed consistently loudest. At that point the Belgians started to dig; and instantly a triumphant shout rent the air. The place was an old disused shaft boarded over and covered with a thin layer of earth. At last it was open, and from it there issued loud and clear a dreadful tapping.

"A network of galleries," cried an interpreter excitedly. "Probably old shafts reaching the German lines. We are lost." He and the commandant had a pouffing match in their despair. But now the noise became greater, and we heard distinctly a human voice. It was at that moment the dread suspicion first dawned on me. An army of men hung over the edge, armed to the teeth with pistols and bowie knives, tin cans and bits of brick. Tap, tap, louder and louder, came the noise. The Pouffers were silent — every one breathed hard.

Then suddenly I heard it echoing along the hollow gallery: "What a faice, what a faice, what a norrible faice — Hebeneezer, you perisher; where the 'ell are you? — lumme, what a faice she 'ad."

" 'The Watch on the Rhine.' They sing their accursed song," howled the commandant, "Belgium for ever, *mes braves!*"

It was at that moment that a stout spectator, moved to frenzy by this appeal, or else owing to a rush of blood to the head, hurled his tin can. Every one fired — a ghastly noise rent the gloom of the well; there was the sound of something departing at a great rate; a heavy fall; and then silence.

I walked thoughtfully back to my dug-out, refusing the offer of making further explorations. As I passed inside I met Brown. He was limping, and the skin was off his nose.

"What have you been doing?" I demanded.

"I fell down, sir," he answered.

"Brown," I said sternly, "where is the goat, Ebeneezer?"

Brown rubbed his nose and looked thoughtfully at me. "Well, sir, I can't say as 'ow I rightly know. 'E *was* —" Further disclosures were nipped in the bud by the sudden appearance of the Major. He was inarticulate [= *speechless*] with rage.

"Get me my revolver," he spluttered. "Get me my revolver. That damn' goat's come back and knocked me down again!"

But Brown had discreetly vanished.

THE LUMBER ROOM
by "Saki"   13½

The children were to be driven, as a special treat, to the sands at Jagborough. Nicholas was not to be of the party; he was in disgrace. Only that morning he had refused to eat his wholesome bread-and-milk on the seemingly frivolous ground that there was a frog in it. Older and wiser and better people had told him that there could not possibly be a frog in his bread-and-milk and that he was not to talk nonsense; he continued, nevertheless, to talk what seemed the veriest nonsense, and described with much detail the coloration and markings of the alleged frog. The dramatic part of the incident was that there really was a frog in Nicholas' basin of bread-and-milk; he had put it there himself, so he felt entitled to know something about it. The sin of taking a frog from the garden and putting it into a bowl of wholesome bread-and-milk was enlarged on at great length, but the fact that stood out clearest in the whole affair, as it presented itself to the mind of Nicholas, was that the older, wiser, and better people had been proved to be profoundly in error in matters about which they had expressed the utmost assurance.

'You said there couldn't possibly be a frog in my bread-and-milk; there *was* a frog in my bread-and-milk,' he repeated, [with the insistence of a skilled tactician who does not intend to shift from favourable ground.]

So his boy-cousin and girl-cousin and his quite uninteresting younger brother were to be taken to Jagborough sands that afternoon and he was to stay at home. His cousins' aunt, who insisted, by an unwarranted stretch of imagination, in styling herself his aunt also, had hastily invented the Jagborough expedition in order to impress on Nicholas the delights that he had justly forfeited by his disgraceful conduct at the breakfast-table. It was her habit, whenever one of the children fell from grace, to improvise something of a festival nature from which the offender would be rigorously debarred; if all the children sinned collectively they were suddenly informed of a circus in a neighbouring town, a circus of unrivalled merit and uncounted elephants, to which, but for their depravity, [= *naughtiness*] they would have been taken that very day.

A few decent tears were looked for on the part of Nicholas when the moment for the departure of the expedition arrived. As a matter of fact, however, all the crying was done by his girl-cousin, who scraped her knee rather painfully against the step of the carriage as she was scrambling in.

"How did she howl," said Nicholas cheerfully, as the party drove off without any of the [elation of] high spirits that should have characterized it.

"She'll soon get over that," said the [*soi-disant*] aunt; "it will be a glorious afternoon for racing about over those beautiful sands. How they will enjoy themselves!"

"Bobby won't enjoy himself much, and he won't race much either," said Nicholas with a grim chuckle; "his boots are hurting him. They're too tight."

"Why didn't he tell me they were hurting?" asked the aunt with some asperity.

"He told you twice, but you weren't listening. You often don't listen when we tell you important things."

"You are not to go into the gooseberry garden," said the aunt, changing the subject.

"Why not?" demanded Nicholas.

"Because you are in disgrace," said the aunt loftily.

Nicholas [did not admit the flawlessness of the reasoning; he] felt perfectly capable of being in disgrace and in a gooseberry garden at the same moment. His face took on an expression of considerable obstinacy. It was clear to his aunt that he was determined to get into the gooseberry garden, "only," as she remarked to herself, "because I have told him he is not to."

Now the gooseberry garden had two doors by which it might be entered, and once a small person like Nicholas could slip in there he could effectually disappear from view amid the masking growth of artichokes, raspberry canes, and fruit bushes. The aunt had many other things to do that afternoon, but she spent an hour or two in trivial gardening operations among flower beds and shrubberies, whence she could keep a watchful eye on the two doors that led to the forbidden paradise. She was a woman of few ideas, with immense powers of concentration.

Nicholas made one or two sorties into the front garden, wriggling his way with obvious stealth of purpose towards one or other of the doors, but never able for a moment to evade the aunt's watchful eye. As a matter of fact, he had no intention of trying to get into the gooseberry garden, but it was extremely convenient for him that his aunt should believe that he had; it was a belief that would keep her on self-imposed sentry-duty for the greater part of the afternoon. Having thoroughly confirmed and fortified her suspicions, Nicholas slipped back into the house and rapidly put into execution a plan of action that had long germinated in his brain. By standing on a chair in the library one could reach a shelf on which reposed a fat, important-looking key. The key was as important as it looked; it was the instrument which kept the mysteries of the lumber-room secure from unauthorized intrusion, which opened a way only for aunts and such-like privileged persons. Nicholas had not had much experience of the art of fitting keys into keyholes and turning locks, but for some days past he had practised with the key of the schoolroom door; he did not believe in trusting too much to luck and accident. The key turned stiffly in the lock, but it turned. The door opened, and Nicholas was in an unknown land, compared with which the gooseberry garden was a stale delight, a mere material pleasure.

Often and often Nicholas had pictured to himself what the lumber-room might be like, that region that was so carefully sealed from youthful eyes and concerning which no questions were ever answered. It came up to his expectations. In the first place it was large and dimly lit, one high window opening onto the forbidden garden being its only source of illumination. In the second place it was a storehouse of unimagined treasures. The aunt-by-assertion was one of those people who think that things spoil by use and consign them to dust and damp by way of preserving them. Such parts of the house as Nicholas knew best were rather bare and cheerless, but here there were wonderful things for the eye to feast on. First and foremost there was a piece of framed tapestry that was evidently meanst to be a fire-screen. To Nicholas it was a living, breathing story; he sat down on a roll of Indian hangings, glowing in wonderful colours beneath a layer of dust, and took in all the details of the tapestry picture. A man, dressed in the hunting costume of some remote period, had just transfixed a stag with an arrow; it could not have been a difficult shot because the stag was only one or two paces away from him; in the thickly growing vegetation that the picture suggested it would not have been difficult to creep up to a feeding stag, and the two spotted dogs that were springing forward to join in the chase had evidently been trained to keep to heel till the arrow was discharged. That part of the picture was simple, if interesting, but did the huntsman see, what Nicholas saw, that four galloping wolves were coming in his direction through the wood? There might be more than four of them hidden behind the trees, and in any case would the man and his dogs be able to cope with the four wolves if they made an attack? The man had only two arrows left in his quiver, and he might miss with one or both of them; all one knew about his skill in shooting was that he could hit a large stag at a ridiculously short range. Nicholas sat for many golden minutes revolving the possibilities of the scene; he was inclined to think that there were more than four wolves and that the man and his dogs were in a tight corner. But there were other objects of delight and interest claiming his instant attention; there were quaint twisted candlesticks in the shape of snakes, and a teapot fashioned like a china duck, out of whose open beak the tea was supposed to come. How dull and shapeless the nursery teapot seemed in comparison! And there was a carved sandalwood box packed tight with aromatic cotton-wool, and between the layers of cotton-wool were little brass figures, hump-necked bulls, and peacocks and goblins, delightful to see and to handle. Less promising in appearance was a large square book with plain black covers; Nicholas peeped into it, and, behold, it was full of coloured pictures of birds. And such birds! In the garden, and in the lanes when he went for a walk, Nicholas came across a few birds, of which the largest were an occasional magpie or wood-pigeon; here were herons and bustards, kites, toucans, tiger-bitterns, brush turkeys, ibises, golden pheasants, a whole portrait gallery of undreamed-of creatures. And as he was admiring the colouring of the mandarin duck and assigning a life-history to it, the voice of his aunt in shrill vociferation of his name came from the gooseberry garden without. She had grown suspicious of his long disappearance, and had leapt to the conclusion that he had climbed over the wall behind the sheltering screen of the lilac bushes; she was now engaged in energetic and rather hopeless search for him among the artichokes and raspberry canes.

"Nicholas, Nicholas!" she screamed, "you are to come out of this at once. It's no use trying hide there; I can see you all the time."

It was probably the first time for twenty years that any one had smiled in that lumber-room.

Presently the angry repetitions of Nicholas' name gave way to a shriek, and a cry for somebody to come quickly. Nicholas shut the bood, restored it carefully to its place in a corner, and shook some dust from a neighbouring pile of newspapers over it. Then he crept from the room, locked the door, and replaced the key exactly where he had found it. His aunt was still calling his name when he sauntered into the front garden.

"Who's calling?" he asked.

"Me," came the answer from the other side of the wall; "didn't you hear me? I've been looking for you in the gooseberry garden, and I've slipped into the rain-water tank. Luckily there's no water in it, but the sides are slippery and I can't get out. Fetch the little ladder from under the cherry tree—"

"I was told I wasn't to go into the gooseberry garden," said Nicholas promptly.

"I told you not to, and now I tell you that you may," came the voice from the rain-water tank, rather impatiently.

"Your voice doesn't sound like aunt's," objected Nicholas; "you may be the Evil One tempting me to be disobedient. Aunt often tells me that the Evil One tempts me and that I always yield. This time I'm not going to yield."

"Don't talk nonsense," said the prisoner in the tank; "go and fetch the ladder."

"Will there be strawberry jam for tea?" asked Nicholas innocently.

"Certainly there will be," said the aunt, privately resolving that Nicholas should have none of it.

"Now I know that you are the Evil One and not aunt," shouted Nicholas gleefully; "when we asked aunt for strawberry jam yesterday she said there wasn't any. I know there are four jars of it in the store cupboard, because I looked, and of course you know it's there, but *she* doesn't, because she said there wasn't any. Oh, Devil, you *have* sold yourself!"

There was an unusual sense of luxury in being able to talk to an aunt as though one was talking to the Evil One, but Nicholas knew, with childish discernment, that such luxuries were not be over-indulged in. He walked noisily away, and it was a kitchenmaid, in search of parsley, who eventually rescued the aunt from the rain-water tank.

Tea that evening was partaken of in a fearsome silence. The tide had been at its highest when the children had arrived at Jagborough Cove, so there had been no sands to play on — a circumstance that the aunt had overlooked in the haste of organizing her punitive expedition. The tightness of Bobby's boots had had disastrous effect on his temper the whole of the afternoon, and altogether the children could not have been said to have enjoyed themselves. The aunt maintained the frozen muteness of one who has suffered undignified and unmerited detention in a rain-water tank for thirty-five minutes. As for Nicholas, he, too, was silent, in the absorption of one who has much to think about; it was just possible, he considered, that the huntsman would escape with his hounds while the wolves feasted on the stricken stag.

SOAKED IN SEAWEED
or UPSET IN THE OCEAN
(An old-fashioned sea story)   20
by Stephen Leacock   [16½]

It was in August in 1867 that I stepped on board the deck of the *Saucy Sally*, lying in dock at Gravesend, to fill the berth of second mate.

Let me first say a word about myself.

I was a tall, handsome young fellow, squarely and powerfully built, bronzed by the sun and the moon (and even copper-coloured in spots from the effect of the stars), and with a face in which honesty, intelligence, and exceptional brain power were combined with Christianity, simplicity, and modesty.

[As I stepped on the deck I could not help a slight feeling of triumph, as I caught sight of my sailor-like features reflected in a tar-barrel that stood beside the mast, while a little later I could scarcely repress a sense of gratification as I noticed them reflected again in a bucket of bilge water.]

"Welcome on board, Mr. Blowhard," called out Captain Bilge, stepping out of the binnacle and shaking hands across the taffrail.

I saw before me a fine sailor-like man of from thirty to sixty, clean-shaven, except for an enormous pair of whiskers, a heavy beard, and a thick moustache, powerful in build, and carrying his beam well aft, in a pair of broad duck trousers across the back of which there would have been room to write a history of the British Navy.

Beside him were the first and third mates, both of them being quiet men of poor stature, who looked at Captain Bilge with what seemed to me an apprehensive expression in their eyes.

The vessel was on the eve of departure. Her deck presented that scene of bustle and alacrity dear to the sailor's heart. Men were busy nailing up the masts, hanging the bowsprit over the side, varnishing the lee-scuppers and pouring hot tar down the companion-way.

[Captain Bilge, with a megaphone to his lips, kept calling out to the men in his rough sailor fashion:

"Now, then, don't over-exert yourselves, gentlemen. Remember, please, that we have plenty of time. Keep out of the sun as much as you can. Step carefully in the rigging there, Jones; I fear it's just a little high for you. Tut, tut, Williams, don't get yourself so dirty with that tar, you won't look fit to be seen."]

I stood leaning over the gaff of the mainsail and thinking — yes, thinking, dear reader, of my mother. I hope that you will think none the less of me for that. Whenever things look dark, I lean up against something and think of mother. If they get positively black, I stand on one leg and think of father. After that I can face anything.

[Did I think, too, of another, younger than mother and fairer than father? Yes, I did. "Bear up, darling," I had whispered as she nestled her head beneath my oilskins and kicked out backward with one heel in the agony of her girlish grief, "in five years the voyage will be over, and after three more

C

like it, I shall come back with money enough to buy a second-hand fishing-net and settle down on shore."]

Meantime the ship's preparations were complete. The masts were all in position, the sails nailed up, and men with axes were busily chopping away the gangway.

"All ready?" called the Captain.

"Aye, aye, sir."

"Then hoist the anchor in board and send a man down with the key to open the bar."

[Opening the bar! the last sad rite of departure. How often in my voyages have I seen it; the little group of men soon to be exiled from their home, standing about with saddened faces, waiting to see the man with the key open the bar — held there by some strange fascination.]

Next morning with a fair wind astern we had buzzed around the corner of England and were running down the Channel.

I know no finer sight, for those who have never seen it, than the English Channel. It is the highway of the world. Ships of all nations are passing up and down, Dutch, Scotch, Venezuelan, and even American.

Chinese junks rush to and fro. Warships, motor yachts, icebergs, and lumber rafts are everywhere. If I add to this fact that so thick a fog hangs over it that it is entirely hidden from sight, my readers can form some idea of the majesty of the scene.

We had now been three days at sea. My first sea-sickness was wearing off, and I thought less of father.

On the third morning Captain Bilge descended to my cabin.

"Mr. Blowhard," he said, "I must ask you to stand double watches."

"What is the matter?" I inquired.

"The two other mates have fallen overboard," he said uneasily, and avoiding my eye.

I contented myself with saying, "Very good, sir," but I could not help thinking it a trifle odd that both the mates should have fallen overboard in the same night.

Surely there was some mystery in this.

Two mornings later the Captain appeared at the breakfast-table with the same shifting and uneasy look in his eye.

"Anything wrong, sir?" I asked.

"Yes," he answered, trying to appear at ease [and twisting a fried egg to and fro between his fingers with such nervous force as almost to break it in two –] "I regret to say that we have lost the bosun."

"The bosun!" I cried.

"Yes," said Captain Bilge more quietly, "he is overboard. I blame myself for it, partly. It was early this morning. I was holding him up in my arms to look at an iceberg, and, quite accidentally I assure you – I dropped him overboard."

"Captain Bilge," I asked, "have you taken any steps to recover him?"

"Not as yet," he replied uneasily.

I looked at him fixedly, but said nothing.

Ten days passed.

The mystery thickened. On Thursday two men of the starboard watch were reported missing. On Friday the carpenter's assistant disappeared. On the night of Saturday a circumstance occurred which, slight as it was, gave me some clue as to what was happening.

As I stood at the wheel about midnight, I saw the Captain approach in the darkness carrying the cabin-boy by the hind leg. The lad was a bright little fellow, whose merry disposition had already endeared him to me, and I watched with some interest to see what the Captain would do to him. Arrived at the stern of the vessel, Captain Bilge looked cautiously around a moment and then dropped the boy into the sea. For a brief instant the lad's head appeared in the phosphorus of the waves. The Captain threw a boot at him, sighed deeply, and went below.

Here then was the key to the mystery! The Captain was throwing the crew overboard. Next morning we met at breakfast as usual.

"Poor little Williams has fallen overboard," said the Captain, seizing a strip of ship's bacon and tearing at it with his teeth as if he almost meant to eat it.

"Captain," I said, greatly excited, [stabbing at a ship's loaf in my agitation with such ferocity as almost to drive my knife into it –] "You threw that boy overboard!"

"I did," said Captain Bilge, grown suddenly quiet, "I threw them all over and intend to throw the rest. Listen, Blowhard, you are young, ambitious, and trustworthy. I will confide in you."

Perfectly calm now, he stepped to a locker, rummaged in it a moment, and drew out a faded piece of yellow parchment, which he spread on the table. It was a map or chart. In the centre of it was a circle. In the middle of the circle was a small dot and a letter T, while at one side of the map was a letter N, and against it on the other side a letter S.

"What is this?" I asked.

"Can you not guess?" queried Captain Bilge. "It is a desert island."

"Ah!" I rejoined with a sudden flash of intuition, "and N is for North and S is for South."

"Blowhard," said the Captain, striking the table with such force as to cause a loaf of ship's bread to bounce up and down three or four times, "you've struck it. That part of it had not yet occurred to me."

"And the letter T?" I asked.

"The treasure, the buried treasure," said the Captain, and turning the map over he read from the back of it — "The point T indicates the spot where the treasure is buried under the sand; it consists of half a million Spanish dollars, and is buried in a brown leather dress-suit case."

"And where is the island?" I inquired, mad with excitement.

"That I do not know," said the Captain. "I intend to sail up and down the parallels of latitude until I find it."

"And meantime?"

"Meantime, the first thing to do is to reduce the number of the crew so as to have fewer hands to divide among. Come, come," he added in a burst of frankness which made me love the man in spite of his shortcomings, "will you join me in this? We'll throw them all over, keeping the cook to the last, dig up the treasure, and be rich for the rest of our lives."

Reader, do you blame me if I said yes? I was young, ardent, ambitious, full of bright hopes and boyish enthusiasm.

"Captain Bilge," I said, putting my hand in his, "I am yours."

["Good," he said, "now go forward to the forecastle and get an idea what the men are thinking."

I went forward to the men's quarters — a plain room in the front of the ship, with only a rough carpet on the floor, a few simple armchairs, writing-desks, spittoons of a plain pattern, and small brass beds with blue-and-green screens. It was Sunday morning, and the men were mostly sitting about in their dressing gowns.

They rose as I entered and curtseyed.

"Sir," said Tompkins, the bosun's mate, "I think it is my duty to tell you that there is a great deal of dissatisfaction among the men."

Several of the men nodded.

"They don't like the way the men keep going overboard," he continued, his voice rising to a tone of uncontrolled passion. "It is positively absurd, sir, and if you will allow me to say so, the men are far from pleased."

"Tompkins," I said sternly, "you must understand that my position will not allow me to listen to mutinous language of this sort."

I returned to the Captain. "I think the men mean mutiny," I said.

"Good," said Captain Bilge, rubbing his hands, "that will get rid of a lot of them, and of course," he added musingly, looking out of the broad old-fashioned port-hole at the stern of the cabin, at the heaving waves of the South Atlantic, "I am expecting pirates at any time, and that will take out quite a few of them. However" — and here he pressed the bell for a cabin-boy — "kindly ask Mr Tompkins to step this way."

"Tompkins," said the Captain as the bosun's mate entered, "be good enough to stand on the locker and stick your head through the stern port-hole, and tell me what you think of the weather."

"Aye, aye, sir," replied the tar with a simplicity which caused us to exchange a quiet smile.

Tompkins stood on the locker and put his head and shoulders out of the port.

Taking a leg each we pushed him through. We heard him plump into the sea.

"Tompkins was easy," said Captain Bilge. "Excuse me as I enter his death in the log."

"Yes," he continued presently, "it will be a great help if they mutiny. I suppose they will, sooner or later. It's customary to do so. But I shall take no step to precipitate it until we have first fallen in with pirates. I am expecting them in these latitudes at any time. Meantime, Mr. Blowhard," he said, rising, "if you can continue to drop overboard one or two more each week, I shall feel extremely grateful."]

Three days later we rounded the Cape of Good Hope and entered upon the inky waters of the Indian Ocean. Our course lay now in zigzags and, the weather being favourable, we sailed up and down at a furious rate over a sea as calm as glass.

On the fourth day a pirate ship appeared. Reader, I do not know if you have ever seen a pirate ship. The sight was one to appal the stoutest heart. The entire ship was painted black, a black flag hung at the masthead, the sails were black, and on the deck people dressed all in black walked up and down arm-in-arm. The words "Pirate Ship" were painted in white letters on the bow. At the sight of it our crew were visibly cowed. It was a spectacle that would have cowed a dog.

The two ships were brought side by side. They were then lashed tightly together with bag string and binder twine, and a gang plank laid between them. In a moment the pirates swarmed upon our deck, rolling their eyes, gnashing their teeth and filing their nails.

Then the fight began. It lasted two hours — with fifteen minutes off for lunch. It was awful. The men grappled with one another, kicked one another from behind, slapped one another across the face, and in many cases completely lost their temper and tried to bite one another. I noticed one gigantic fellow brandishing a knotted towel, and striking right and left among our men, until Captain Bilge rushed at him and struck him flat across the mouth with a banana skin.

At the end of two hours, by mutual consent, the fight was declared a draw. The points standing at sixty-one and a half against sixty-two.

The ships were unlashed, and with three cheers from each crew, were headed on their way.

"Now, then," said the Captain to me aside, "let us see how many of the crew are sufficiently exhausted to be thrown overboard."

He went below. In a few minutes he returned, his face deadly pale. "Blowhard," he said, "the ship is sinking. One of the pirates (sheer accident, of course, I blame no one) has kicked a hole in the side. Let us sound the well."

We put our ear to the ship's well. It sounded like water.

The men were put to the pumps and worked with the frenzied effort which only those who have been drowned in a sinking ship can understand.

At six p.m. the well marked one half an inch of water, at nightfall three-quarters of an inch, and at daybreak, after a night of unremitting toil, seven-eighths of an inch.

By noon of the next day the water had risen to fifteen-sixteenths of an inch, and on the next night the sounding showed thirty-one thirty-seconds of an inch of water in the hold. The situation was desperate. At this rate of increase few, if any, could tell where it would rise to in a few days.

That night the Captain called me to his cabin. He had a book of mathematical tables in front of him, and great sheets of vulgar fractions littered the floor on all sides.

"The ship is bound to sink," he said, "in fact, Blowhard, she is sinking. I can prove it. It may be six months or it may take years, but if she goes on like this, sink she must. There is nothing for it but to abandon her."

That night, in the dead of darkness, while the crew were busy at the pumps, the Captain and I built a raft.

Unobserved we cut down the masts, chopped them into suitable lengths, laid them crosswise in a pile and lashed them tightly together with bootlaces.

Hastily we threw on board a couple of boxes of food and bottles of drinking fluid, a sextant, a chronometer, a gas-meter, a bicycle pump and a few other scientific instruments. Then taking advantage of a roll in the motion of the ship, we launched the raft, lowered ourselves upon a line and under cover of the heavy dark of a tropical night, we paddled away from the doomed vessel.

The break of day found us a tiny speck on the Indian Ocean. [We looked about as big as this (.).]

In the morning, after dressing, and shaving as best we could, we opened our box of food and drink.

Then came the awful horror of our situation.

One by one the Captain took from the box the square blue tins of canned beef which it contained. We counted fifty-two in all. Anxiously and with drawn faces we watched until the last can was lifted from the box. A single thought was in our minds. When the end came the Captain stood up on the raft with wild eyes staring at the sky.

"The can-opener!" he shrieked, "just Heaven, the can-opener." He fell prostrate.

Meantime, with trembling hands, I opened the box of bottles. It contained lager beer bottles, each with a patent tin top. One by one I took them out. There were fifty-two in all. As I withdrew the last one and saw the empty box before me, I shroke out — "The thing! the thing! oh, merciful Heaven! The thing you open them with!"

I fell prostrate upon the Captain.

We awoke to find ourselves still a mere speck upon the ocean. We felt even smaller than before.

Over us was the burnished copper sky of the tropics. The heavy, leaden sea lapped the sides of the raft. All about us was a litter of corn beef cans and lager beer bottles. Our sufferings in the ensuing days were indescribable. We beat and thumped at the cans with our fists. Even at the risk of spoiling the tins for ever we hammered them fiercely against the raft. We stamped on them, bit at them and swore at them. We pulled and clawed at the bottles with our hands, and chipped and knocked them against the cans, regardless even of breaking the glass and ruining the bottles.

It was futile.

Then day after day we sat in moody silence, gnawed with hunger, with nothing to read, nothing to smoke, and practically nothing to talk about.

On the tenth day the Captain broke silence.

"Get ready the lots, Blowhard," he said. "It's got to come to that."

"Yes," I answered drearily, "we're getting thinner every day."

Then, with the awful prospect of cannibalism before us, we drew lots.

I prepared the lots and held them to the Captain. He drew the longer one.

"Which does that mean," he asked, trembling between hope and despair. "Do I win?"

"No, Bilge," I said sadly, "you lose."

But I mustn't dwell on the days that followed — the long quiet days of lazy dreaming on the raft, during which I slowly built up my strength, which had been shattered by privation. They were days, dear reader, of deep and quiet peace, and yet I cannot recall them without shedding a tear for the brave man who made them what they were.

It was on the fifth day after that I was awakened from a sound sleep by the bumping of the raft against the shore. I had eaten perhaps overheartily, and had not observed the vicinity of land.

Before me was an island, the circular shape of which, with its low, sandy shore, recalled at once its identity.

"The treasure island," I cried, "at last I am rewarded for all my heroism."

In a fever of haste I rushed to the centre of the island. What was the sight that confronted me? A great hollow scooped in the sand, an empty dress-suit case lying beside it, and on a ship's plank driven deep in the sand, the legend, "*Saucy Sally*, October, 1867." So! the miscreants had made good the vessel, headed it for the island of whose existence they must have learned from the chart we so carelessly left on the cabin table, and had plundered poor Bilge and me of our well-earned treasure!

Sick with the sense of human ingratitude I sank upon the sand.

The island became my home.

There I eked out a miserable existence, feeding on sand and gravel and dressing myself in cactus plants. Years passed. Eating sand and mud slowly undermined my robust constitution. I fell ill. I died. I buried myself.

Would that others who write sea stories would do as much.

THE DEVOTED FRIEND

by Oscar Wilde

21½
[16½]

[One morning the old Water-rat put his head out of his hole. He had bright beady eyes and stiff grey whiskers, and his tail was like a long bit of black india rubber. The little ducks were swimming about in the pond, looking just like a lot of yellow canaries, and their mother, who was pure white with real red legs, was trying to teach them how to stand on their heads in the water.

"You will never be in the best society unless you can stand on your head," she kept saying to them; and every now and then she showed them how it was done. But the little ducks paid no attention to her. They were so young that they did not know what an advantage it is to be in society at all.

"What disobedient children!" cried the old Water-rat; "they really deserve to be drowned."

"Nothing of the kind," answered the Duck; "everyone must make a beginning, and parents cannot be too patient."

"Ah! I know nothing about the feelings of parents," said the Water-rat: "I am not a family man. In fact, I have never been married, and I never intend to be. Love is all very well in its way, but friendship is much higher. Indeed, I know of nothing in the world that is either nobler or rarer than a devoted friendship."

"And what, pray, is your idea of the duties of a devoted friend?" asked a green Linnet, who was sitting on a willow-tree hard by, and had overhead the conversation.

"Yes, that is just what I want to know," said the Duck; and she swam away to the end of the pond, and stood upon her head, in order to give her children a good example.

"What a silly question!" cried the Water-rat. "I should expect my devoted friend to be devoted to me, of course."

"And what would you do in return?" said the little bird, swinging upon a silver spray, and flapping his tiny wings.

"I don't understand you," answered the Water-rat.

"Let me tell you a story on the subject," said the Linnet.

"Is the story about me?" asked the Water-rat. "If so, I will listen to it, for I am extremely fond of fiction."

"It is applicable to you," answered the Linnet; and he flew down, and, alighting upon the bank, he told the story of The Devoted Friend.]

"Once upon a time," [said the Linnet,] "there was an honest little fellow named Hans."

["Was he very distinguished?" asked the Water-rat.

"No," answered the Linnet, "I don't think he was distinguished at all, except for his kind heart, and his funny, round, good-humoured face.] He lived in a tiny cottage all by himself, and every day he worked in his garden. In all the countryside there was no garden so lovely as his. [Sweet-Williams grew there, and Gilly-flowers, and Shepherds'-purses, and Fair-maids of France. There were damask Roses, and yellow Roses, lilac Crocuses and gold, purple Violets and white. Columbine and Ladysmock, Marjoram and Wild Basil, the Cowslip and the Flower-de-luce, the Daffodil and the Clove-Pink bloomed or blossomed in their proper order as the months went by, one flower taking another flower's place, so that there were always beautiful things to look at, and pleasant odours to smell.]

"Little Hans had a great many friends, but the most devoted friend of all was big Hugh the Miller. Indeed, so devoted was the rich Miller to little Hans, that he would never go by his garden without leaning over the wall and plucking a large nosegay, or a handful of sweet herbs, or filling his pockets with plums and cherries if it was the fruit season.

" 'Real friends should have everything in common,' the Miller used to say, and little Hans nodded and smiled, and felt very proud of having a friend with such noble ideas.

"Sometimes, indeed, the neighbours thought it strange that the rich Miller never gave little Hans anything in return, though he had a hundred sacks of flour stored away in his mill, and six milch cows, and a large flock of woolly sheep; but Hans never troubled his head about these things, and nothing gave him greater pleasure than to listen to all the wonderful things the Miller used to say about the unselfishness of true friendship.

"So little Hans worked away in his garden. During the spring, the summer, and the autumn he was very happy, but when the winter came, and he had no fruit or flowers to bring to the market, he suffered a good deal from cold and hunger, and often had to go to bed without any supper but a few dried pears or some hard nuts. In the winter, also, he was extremely lonely, as the

Miller never came to see him then.

" 'There is no good in my going to see little Hans as long as the snow lasts,' the Miller used to say to his wife, 'for when people are in trouble they should be left alone and not be bothered by visitors. That at least is my idea about friendship, and I am sure I am right. So I shall wait till the spring comes, and then I shall pay him a visit, and he will be able to give me a large basket of primroses, and that will make him so happy.'

" 'You are certainly very thoughtful about others,' answered the Wife, as she sat in her comfortable armchair by the big pinewood fire; 'very thoughtful indeed. It is quite a treat to hear you talk about friendship. I am sure the clergyman himself could not say such beautiful things as you do, though he does live in a three-storied house, and wear a gold ring on his little finger.'

" 'But could we not ask little Hans up here?' said the Miller's youngest son. 'If poor Hans is in trouble I will give him half my porridge, and show him my white rabbits.'

" 'What a silly boy you are!' cried the Miller; 'I really don't know what is the use of sending you to school. You seem not to learn anything. Why, if little Hans came up here, and saw our warm fire, and our good supper, and our great cask of red wine, he might get envious, and envy is a most terrible thing, and would spoil anybody's nature. I certainly will not allow Hans' nature to be spoiled. I am his best friend, and I will always watch over him, and see that he is not led into any temptations. Besides, if Hans came here, he might ask me to let him have some flour on credit, and that I could not do. Flour is one thing, and friendship is another, and they should not be confused. Why, the words are spelt differently, and mean quite different things. Everybody can see that.'

" 'How well you talk!' said the Miller's Wife, pouring herself out a large glass of warm ale; 'really I feel quite drowsy. It is just like being church.'

" 'Lots of people act well,' answered the Miller; 'but very few people talk well, which shows that talking is much the more difficult thing of the two, and much the finer thing also'; and he looked sternly across the table at his little son, who felt so ashamed of himself that he hung his head down, and grew quite scarlet and began to cry into his tea. However, he was so young that you must excuse him.'

["Is that the end of the story?" asked the Water-rat.

"Certainly not," answered the Linnet, "that is the beginning."

"Then you are quite behind the age," said the Water-rat. "Every good storyteller nowadays starts with the end, and then goes on to the beginning, and concludes with the middle. That is the new method. I heard all about it the other day from a critic who was walking round the pond with a young man. He spoke of the matter at great length, and I am sure he must have been right, for he had blue spectacles and a bald head, and whenever the young man made any remark, he always answered "Pooh!" But pray go on with your story. I like the Miller immensely. I have all kinds of beautiful sentiments myself, so there is a great sympathy between us."

"Well," said the Linnet, hopping now one leg and now on the other,] "as soon as the winter was over, and the primroses began to open their pale yellow stars, the Miller said to his wife that he would go down and see little Hans.

" 'Why, what a good heart you have!' cried his Wife; 'you are always thinking of others. And mind you take the big basket with you for the flowers.'

"So the Miller tied the sails of the windmill together with a strong iron chain, and went down the hill with the basket on his arm.

' "Good morning, little Hans,' said the Miller.

" 'Good morning,' said Hans, leaning on his spade, and smiling from ear to ear.

" 'And how have you been all the winter?' said the Miller.

" 'Well, really,' cried Hans, 'it is very good of you to ask, very good indeed. I am afraid I had rather a hard time of it, but now the spring has come, and I am quite happy, and all my flowers are doing well.'

" 'We often talked of you during the winter, Hans,' said the Miller, 'and wondered how you were getting on.'

" 'That was kind of you,' said Hans; 'I was half afraid you had forgotten me.'

" 'Hans, I am surprised at you,' said the Miller; 'friendship never forgets. That is the wonderful thing about it, but I am afraid you won't understand the poetry of life. How lovely your primroses are looking, by-the-bye!'

" 'They are certainly very lovely,' said Hans, 'and it is a most lucky thing for me that I have so many. I am going to bring them into the market and sell them to the Burgomaster's daughter, and buy back my wheelbarrow with the money.'

" 'Buy back your wheelbarrow? You don't meant to say you have sold it? What a very stupid thing to do!'

" 'Well, the fact is,' said Hans, 'that I was obliged to. You see the winter was a very bad time for me, and I really had no money at all to buy bread with. So I first sold the silver buttons off my Sunday coat, and then I sold my silver chain, and then I sold my big pipe, and at last I sold my wheelbarrow. But I am going to buy them all back again now.'

" 'Hans,' said the Miller, 'I will give you my wheelbarrow. It is not in very good repair, indeed, one side is gone, and there is something wrong with the wheel-spokes, but in spite of that I will give it to you. I know it is very generous of me, and a great many people would think me extremely foolish for parting with it, but I am not like the rest of the world. I think that generosity is the essence of friendship, and, besides, I have got a new wheelbarrow for myself. Yes, you may set your mind at ease, I will give you my wheelbarrow.'

" 'Well, really, that is generous of you,' said little Hans, and his funny round face glowed all over with pleasure. 'I can easily put it in repair, as I have a plank of wood in the house.'

" 'A plank of wood!' said the Miller; 'why, that is just what I want for the roof of my barn. There is a very large hole in it, and the corn will all get damp if I don't stop it up. How lucky you mentioned it! It is quite remarkable how one good action always breeds another. I have given you my wheelbarrow, and now you are going to give me your plank. Of course, the wheelbarrow is worth far more than the plank, but true friendship never notices things like that. Pray get it at once, and I will set to work at my barn this very day.'

" 'Certainly,' cried little Hans, and he ran into the shed and dragged the plank out.

" 'It is not a very big plank,' said the Miller, looking at it, 'and I am afraid that after I have mended my barn-roof there won't be any left for you to mend the wheelbarrow with; but, of course, that is not my fault. And now, as I have given you my wheelbarrow, I am sure you would like to give me some flowers in return. Here is the basket, and mind you fill it quite full.'

" 'Quite full?' said little Hans, rather sorrowfully, for it was really a very big basket, and he knew that if he filled it he would have no flowers left for the market, and he was very anxious to get his silver buttons back.

" 'Well, really,' answered the Miller, 'as I have given you my wheelbarrow, I don't think that it is much to ask you for a few flowers. I may be wrong, but I should have thought that friendship, true friendship, was quite free from selfishness of any kind.'

" 'My dear friend, my best friend,' cried little Hans, 'you are welcome to all the flowers in my garden. I would much sooner have your good opinion than my silver buttons, any day'; and he ran and plucked all his pretty primroses, and filled the Miller's basket.

" 'Good-bye, little Hans,' said the Miller, and he went up the hill with the plank on his shoulder, and the big basket in his hand.

" 'Good-bye,' said little Hans, and he began to dig away quite merrily, he was so pleased about the wheel-barrow.

"The next day he was nailing up some honeysuckle against the porch, when he heard the Miller's voice calling to him from the road. So he jumped off the ladder, and ran down the garden, and looked over the wall.

"There was the Miller with a large sack of flour on his back.

" 'Dear little Hans,' said the Miller, 'would you mind carrying this sack of flour for me to market?'

" 'Oh, I am so sorry,' said Hans, 'but I am really very busy today. I have got all my creepers to nail up, and all my flowers to water, and all my grass to roll.'

" 'Well, really,' said the Miller, 'I think, that considering that I am going to give you my wheelbarrow it is rather unfriendly of you to refuse.'

" 'Oh, don't say that,' cried little Hans, 'I wouldn't be unfriendly for the whole world;' and he ran in for his cap, and trudged off with the big sack on his shoulders.

"It was a very hot day, and the road was terribly dusty, and before Hans had reached the sixth milestone he was so tired that he had to sit down and rest. However, he went on bravely, and at last he reached the market. After he had waited there for some time, he sold the sack of flour for a very good price, and then he returned home at once, for he was afraid that if he stopped too late he might meet some robbers on the way.

" 'It has certainly been a hard day,' said little Hans to himself as he was going to bed, 'but I am glad I did not refuse the Miller, for he is my best friend and, besides, he is going to give me his wheelbarrow.'

"Early the next morning the Miller came down to get the money for his sack of flour, but little Hans was so tired that he was still in bed.

" 'Upon my word,' said the Miller, 'you are very lazy. Really, considering that I am going to give you my wheelbarrow, I think you might work harder. Idleness is a great sin, and I certainly don't like any of my friends to be idle or sluggish. You must not mind my speaking quite plainly to you. Of course I should not dream of doing so if I were not your friend. But what is the good of friendship if one cannot say exactly what one means? Anybody can say charming things and try to please and to flatter, but a true friend always says unpleasant things, and does not mind giving pain. Indeed, if he is a really true friend he prefers it, for he knows that then he is doing good.'

" 'I am very sorry,' said little Hans, rubbing his eyes and pulling off his nightcap, 'but I was so tired that I thought I would lie in bed for a little time, and listen to the birds singing. Do you know that I always work better after hearing the birds sing?'

" 'Well, I am glad of that,' said the Miller, clapping little Hans on the back, 'for I want you to come up to the mill as soon as you are dressed and mend my barn-roof for me.'

"Poor little Hans was very anxious to go and work in his garden, for his flowers had not been watered for two days, but he did not like to refuse the Miller, as he was such a good friend to him.

" 'Do you think it would be unfriendly of me if I said I was busy?' he inquired in a shy and timid voice.

" 'Well, really,' answered the Miller, 'I do not think it is much to ask of you, considering that I am going to give you my wheelbarrow, but, of course, if you refuse I will go and do it myself.'

" 'Oh! on no account,' cried little Hans; and he jumped out of bed, and dressed himself, and went up to the barn.

"He worked there all day long, till sunset, and at sunset the Miller came to see how he was getting on.

" 'Have you mended the hole in the roof yet, little Hans?' cried the Miller in a cheery voice.

" 'It is quite mended,' answered little Hans, coming down the ladder.

" 'Ah!' said the Miller, 'there is no work so delightful as the work one does for others.'

" 'It is certainly a great privilege to hear you talk,' answered little Hans, sitting down and wiping his forehead, 'a very great privilege. But I am afraid I shall never have such beautiful ideas as you have.'

" 'Oh! they will come to you,' said the Miller, 'but you must take more pains. At present you have only the practice of friendship; some day you will have the theory also.'

" 'Do you really think I shall?' asked little Hans.

" 'I have no doubt of it,' answered the Miller, 'but now that you have mended the roof, you had better go home and rest, for I want you to drive my sheep to the mountain tomorrow.'

"Poor little Hans was afraid to say anything to this, and early the next morning the Miller brought his sheep round to the cottage, and Hans started off with them to the mountain. It took him the whole day to get there and back; and when he returned he was so tired that he went off to sleep in his chair, and did not wake up till it was broad daylight.

" 'What a delightful time I shall have in my garden!' he said, and he went to work at once.

"But somehow he was never able to look after his flowers at all, for his friend the Miller was always coming round and sending him off on long errands, or getting him to help at the mill. Little Hans was very much distressed at times, as he was afraid his flowers would think he had forgotten them, but he consoled himself by the reflection that the Miller was his best friend. 'Besides' he used to say, 'he is going to give me his wheelbarrow, and that is an act of pure generosity.'

"So little Hans worked away for the Miller, and the Miller said all kinds of beautiful things about friendship, which Hans took down in a notebook, and used to read over at night. for he was a very good scholar.

"Now it happened that one evening little Hans was sitting by his fireside when a loud rap came at the door. It was a very wild night, and the wind was blowing and roaring round the house so terribly that at first he thought it was merely the storm. But a second rap came, and then a third, louder than any of the others.

" 'It is some poor traveller,' said little Hans to himself, and he ran to the door.

"There stood the Miller with a lantern in one hand and a big stick in the other.

" 'Dear little Hans,' cried the Miller, 'I am in great trouble. My little boy has fallen off a ladder and hurt himself, and I am going for the Doctor. But he lives so far away, and it is such a bad night, that it has just occurred to me that it would be much better if you went instead of me. You know I am going to give you my wheelbarrow, and so it is only fair that you should do something for me in return.'

" 'Certainly,' cried little Hans, 'I take it quite as a compliment your coming to me, and I will start off at once. But you must lend me your lantern, as the night is so dark that I am afraid I might fall into the ditch.'

" 'I am very sorry,' answered the Miller, 'but it is my new lantern, and it would be a great loss to me if anything happened to it.'

" 'Well, never mind, I will do without it,' cried little Hans, and he took down his great fur coat, and his warm scarlet cap, and tied a muffler round his throat, and started off.

"What a dreadful storm it was! The night was so black that little Hans could hardly see, and the wind was so strong that he could hardly stand. However, he was very courageous, and after he had been walking about three hours, he arrived at the Doctor's house, and knocked at the door.

" 'Who is there?' cried the Doctor, putting his head out of his bedroom window.

" 'Little Hans, Doctor.'

" 'What do you want, little Hans?'

" 'The Miller's son has fallen from a ladder, and has hurt himself, and the Miller wants you to come at once.'

" 'All right!' said the Doctor; and he ordered his horse, and his big boots, and his lantern, and came down-stairs, and rode off in the direction of the Miller's house, little Hans trudging behind him.

"But the storm grew worse and worse, and the rain fell in torrents, and little Hans could not see where he was going, or keep up with the horse. At last he lost his way, and wandered off on the moor, which was a very dangerous place, as it was full of deep holes, and there poor little Hans was drowned. His body was found the next day by some goatherds, floating in a great pool of water, and was brought back by them to the cottage.

"Everybody went to little Hans' funeral, as he was so popular; and the Miller was the chief mourner.

" 'As I was his best friend,' said the Miller, 'it is only fair that I should have the best place'; so he walked at the head of the procession in a long black cloak, and every now and then he wiped his eyes with a big pocket-handkerchief.

" 'Little Hans is certainly a great loss to everyone,' said the Blacksmith, when the funeral was over, and they were all seated comfortably in the inn, drinking spiced wine and eating sweet cakes.

" 'A great loss to me at any rate,' answered the Miller; 'why, I had as good as given him my wheelbarrow, and now I really don't know what to do with it. It is very much in my way at home, and it is in such bad repair that I could not get anything for it if I sold it. I will certainly take care not to give away anything again. One certainly suffers for being generous.'

["Well?" said the Water-rat, after a long pause.

"Well, that is the end," said the Linnet.

"But what became of the Miller?" asked the Water-rat.

"Oh! I really don't know," replied the Linnet; "and I am sure that I don't care."

"It is quite evident then that you have no sympathy in your nature," said the Water-rat.

"I am afraid you don't quite see the moral of the story," remarked the Linnet.

"The what?" screamed the Water-rat.

"The moral."

"Do you mean to say that the story has a moral?"

"Certainly," said the Linnet.

"Well, really," said the Water-rat, in a very angry manner, "I think you should have told me that before you began. If you had done so, I certainly would not have listened to you; in fact, I should have said 'Pooh,' like the critic. However, I can say it now"; so he shouted out "Pooh," at the top of his voice, gave a whisk with his tail, and went back into his hole.

"And how do you like the Water-rat?" asked the Duck, who came paddling up some minutes afterward. "He has a great many good points, but for my own part I have a mother's feelings, and I can never look at a confirmed bachelor without the tears coming into my eyes."

"I am rather afraid that I have annoyed him," answered the Linnet. "The fact is that I told him a story with a moral."

"Ah! that is always a very dangerous thing to do," said the Duck.

And I quite agree with her.]

KNIGHTS ERRANT

from "The Sword in the Stone"   34
by T.H. White   [8]

Wart is the young Arthur, growing up in Sir Ector's castle with his son Kay, and being tutored by Merlyn.

[Tilting and horsemanship had two afternoons a week, because they were the most important branches of a gentleman's education in those days. Merlyn grumbled about athletics, saying that nowadays people seemed to think that you were an educated man if you could knock another man off a horse and that the craze for games was the ruin of scholarship — and nobody got scholarships like they used to do when he was a boy, and all 'the public schools had been forced to lower their standards — but Sir Ector, who was an old tilting blue, said that the battle of Crécy had been won upon the playing fields of Camelot. This made Merlyn so furious that he gave Sir Ector rheumatism two nights running before he relented. Tilting was a great art and needed practice. When two knights jousted they held their lances in their right hands, but they directed their horses at one another so that each man had his opponent on his near side. The base of the lance, in fact, was held on the opposite side of the body to the side at which the enemy was charging. This seems rather inside out to anybody who is in the habit say, of opening gates with a hunting-crop, but it had its reasons. For one thing, it meant that the shield was on the left arm, so that the opponents charged shield to shield, fully covered. It also meant that a man could be unhorsed with the side or edge of the lance, in a kind of horizontal swipe, if you did not feel sure of hitting him with your point. This was the humblest or least skilful blow in jousting.

A good jouster, like Lancelot or Tristram, always used the blow of the point, because, although it was liable to miss in unskilful hands, it made contact sooner. If one knight charged with his lance held rigidly sideways, to sweep his opponent out of the sadde, the other knight with his lance held directly forward would knock him down a lance length before the sweep came into effect.

Then there was how to hold the lance for the point stroke. It was no good crouching in the saddle and clutching it in a rigid grip preparatory to the great shock, for if you held it inflexibly like this its point bucked up and down to every movement of your thundering mount and you were practically certain to miss the aim. On the contrary, you had to sit loosely in the saddle with the lance easy and balanced against the horse's motion. It was not until the actual moment of striking that you clamped your knees into the horse's sides, threw your weight forward in your seat, clutched the lance with the whole hand instead of with the finger and thumb, and hugged your right elbow to your side to support the butt.

There was the size of the spear. Obviously a man with a spear one hundred yards long would strike down an opponent with a spear of ten or twelve feet before the latter came anywhere near him. But it would have been impossible to make a spear one hundred yards long and, if made, impossible to carry it. The jouster had to find out the greatest length which he could manage with the greatest speed, and he had to stick to that. Sir Lancelot, who came some time after this part of the story, had several sizes of spear and would call for his Great Spear, or his Lesser Spear as occasion demanded.

There were the places on which the enemy should be hit. In the armoury of The Castle of the Forest Sauvage there was a big picture of a knight in armour with circles round his vulnerable points. These varied with the style of armour, so that you had to study your opponent before the charge and select a point. The good armourers — the best lived in Warrington, and still live near there — were careful to make all the forward or entering sides of their suits convex, so that the spear point glanced off them. Curiously enough, the shields of Gothic suits were more inclined to be concave. It was better that a spear point should stay on the shield, rather than glance off upward or downward, and perhaps hit a more vulnerable point of the body armour. The best place of all for hitting people was on the very crest of the tilting helm, that is, if the person in question were vain enough to have a large metal crest in whose folds and ornaments the point would find a ready lodging. Many were vain enough to have these armorial crests, with bears and dragons or even ships or castles on them, but Sir Lancelot always contented himself with a bare helmet, or a bunch of feathers which would not hold spears, or, on one occasion, a soft lady's sleeve.

It would take too long to go into all the interesting details of proper tilting which the boys had to learn, for in those days you had to be a master of your craft from the bottom upward. You had to know what wood was best for spears, and why, and even how to turn them so that they would not splinter or warp. There were a thousand disputed questions about arms and armour, all of which had to be understood.

Just outside Sir Ector's castle there was a jousting field for tournaments, although there had been no tournaments in it since Kay was born. It was a green meadow, kept short, with a broad grassy bank raised round it on which pavilions could be erected. There was an old wooden grandstand at one side, lifted on stilts for the ladies. At present the field was only used as a practice-ground for tilting, so a quintain had been erected at one end and a ring at the other. The quintain was a wooden saracen on a pole. He was painted with a bright blue face and red beard and glaring eyes. He had a shield in his left hand and a flat wooden sword in his right. If you hit him in the middle of his forehead all was well, but if your lance struck him on the shield or on any part to left or right of the middle line, then he spun round with great rapidity, and usually caught you a wallop with his sword as you galloped by, ducking. His paint was somewhat scratched and the wood picked up over his right eye. The ring was just an ordinary iron ring tied to a kind of gallows by a thread. If you managed to put your point through the ring, the thread broke, and you could canter off proudly with the ring round your spear.

The day was cooler than it had been for some time, for the autumn was almost within sight, and the two boys were in the tilting yard with the master armourer and Merlyn. The master armourer, or sergeant-at-arms, was a stiff, pale, bouncy gentleman with waxed moustaches. He always marched about with his chest stuck out like a pouter pigeon, and he called out . "On the word One —" on every possible occasion. He took great pains to keep his stomach in, and often tripped over his feet because he could not see them over his chest. He was generally making his muscles ripple, which annoyed Merlyn.

Wart lay beside Merlyn in the shade of the grandstand and scratched himself for harvest bugs. The saw-like sickles had only lately been put away, and the wheat stood in stooks of eight among the tall stubble of those times. The Wart still itched. He was also sore about the shoulders and had a burning ear, from making bosh shots at the quintain — for, of course, practice tilting was done without armour. Wart was pleased that it was Kay's turn to go through it now and he lay drowsily in the shade, snoozing, scratching, twitching like a dog and partly attending to the fun.

Merlyn, sitting with his back to all the athleticism, was practising a spell which he had forgotten. It was a spell to make the sergeant's moustaches uncurl, but at present it only uncurled one of them, and the sergeant had not noticed it. He absent-mindedly curled it up again every time Merlyn did the spell, and Merlyn said, "Drat it!" and began again. Once he made the sergeant's ears flap by mistake, and the latter gave a startled look at the sky.

From far off at the other side of the tilting ground the sergeant's voice came floating on the still air.

"Nah, Nah, Master Kay, that ain't it at all. Has you were. Has you were. The spear should be 'eld between the thumb and forefinger of the right 'and, with the shield in line with the seam of the trahser leg. . . ."

The Wart rubbed his sore ear and sighed.

"What are you grieving about?"

"I was not grieving; I was thinking."

"What were you thinking?"

"Oh, it was not anything. I was thinking about Kay learning to be a knight."

82   *Amusing*

"And well you may grieve," exclaimed Merlyn hotly. "A lot of brainless unicorns swaggering about and calling themselves educated just because they can push each other off a horse with a bit of stick! It makes me tired. Why, I believe Sir Ector would have been gladder to get a by-our-lady tilting blue for your tutor, that swings himself along on his knuckles like an anthropoid ape, rather than a magician of known probity and international reputation with first-class honours from every European university. The trouble with the Norman aristocracy is that they are games-mad, that is what it is, games-mad."

He broke off indignantly and deliberately made the sergeant's ears flap slowly twice, in unison.

"I was not thinking quite about that," said the Wart. "As a matter of fact, I was thinking how nice it would be to be a knight, like Kay."

"Well, you will be one soon enough, won't you?" asked the old man, impatiently.

Wart did not answer.

"Won't you?"

Merlyn turned round and looked closely at the boy through his spectacles.

"What is the matter now?" he enquired nastily. His inspection had shown him that his pupil was trying not to cry, and if he spoke in a kind voice he would break down and do it.

"I shall not be a knight," replied the Wart coldly. Merlyn's trick had worked and he no longer wanted to weep: he wanted to kick Merlyn. "I shall not be a knight because I am not a proper son of Sir Ector's. They will knight Kay, and I shall be his squire."

Merlyn's back was turned again, but his eyes were bright behind his spectacles. "Too bad," he said without commiseration.

The Wart burst out with all his thoughts aloud. "Oh," he cried, "but I should have liked to be born with a proper father and mother, so that I could be a knight errant."

"What would you have done?"

"I should have had a splendid suit of armour and dozens of spears and a black horse standing eighteen hands, and I should have called myself the Black Knight. And I should have hoved at a well or a ford or something and made all true knights that came that way to joust with me for the honour of their ladies, and I should have spared them all after I had given them a great fall. And I should live out of doors all the year round in a pavilion, and never do anything but joust and go on quests and bear away the prize at tournaments, and I should not ever tell anybody my name."

"You wife will scarcely enjoy the life."

"Oh, I am not going to have a wife. I think they are stupid.

"I shall have to have a lady-love, though," added the future knight uncomfortably, "so that I can wear her favour in my helm, and do deeds in her honour."

A humblebee came zooming between them, under the grandstand and out into the sunlight.

"Would you like to see some real knights errant?" asked the magician slowly. "Now, for the sake of your education?"

"Oh, I would! We have never even had a tournament since I was here."

"I suppose it could be managed."

"Oh, please do. You could take me to some like you did to the fish."

"I suppose it is educational, in a way."

"It is very educational," said the Wart. "I can't think of anything more educational than to see some real knights fighting. Oh, won't you please do it?"

"Do you prefer any particular knight?"

"King Pellinore," he said immediately. He had a weakness for this gentleman since their strange encounter in the Forest. Merlyn said, "That will do very well. Put your hands to your sides and relax your muscles. *Cabricias arci thurum, catalamus, singulariter, nominativa, haec musa.* Shut your eyes and keep them shut. *Bonus, Bona, Bonum.* Here we go. *Deus Sanctus, est-ne aratio Latinas? Etiam, oui, quare? Pour-quoi? Quai substantivo et adjectivum concordat in generi, numuerum et casus.* Here we are."

While this incantation was going on, the patient felt some queer sensations. First he could hear the sergeant calling out to Kay, "Nah then, nah then, keep the 'eels dahn and swing the body from the 'ips." Then the words got smaller and smaller, as if he were looking at his feet through the wrong end of a telescope, and began to swirl round in a cone, as if they were at the pointed bottom end of a whirlpool which was sucking him into the air. Then there was nothing but a loud rotating roaring and hissing noise which rose to such a tornado that he felt that he could not stand it any more. Finally there was utter silence and Merlyn saying, "Here we are." All this happened in about the time that it would take a sixpenny rocket to start off with its fiery swish, bend down from its climax and disperse itself in thunder and coloured stars. He opened his eyes just at the moment when one would have heard the invisible stick hitting the ground.

They were lying under a beech tree in the Forest Sauvage.

"Here we are," said Merlyn. "Get up and dust your clothes.

"And there, I think," continued the magician, in a tone of satisfaction because his spells had worked for once without a hitch, "is your friend, King Pellinore, pricking toward us o'er the plain."

"Hallo, hallo," cried King Pellinore, popping his visor up and down. "It's the young boy with the feather bed, isn't it, I say, what?"

"Yes, it is," said the Wart. "And I am very glad to see you. Did you manage to catch the Beast?"

"No," said King Pellinore. "Didn't catch the beast. Oh, do come here, you brachet, and leave that bush alone. Tcha! Tcha! Naughty, naughty! She runs riot, you know, what. Very keen on rabbits. I tell you there's nothing in it, you beastly dog. Tcha! Tcha! Leave it, leave it! Oh, do come to heel, like I tell you.

"She never does come to heel," he added.

At this the dog put a cock pheasant out of the bush, which rocketed off with a tremendous clatter, and the dog became so excited that it ran round its master three or four times at the end of its rope, panting hoarsely as if it had asthma. King Pellinore's horse stood patiently while the rope was wound round its legs, and Merlyn and the Wart had to catch the brachet and unwind it before the conversation could go on.

"I say," said King Pellinore. "Thank you very much. I must say. Won't you introduce me to your friend, what?"

"This is my tutor Merlyn, a great magician."

"How-de-do," said the King. "Always like to meet magicians. In fact I always like to meet anybody. It passes the time away, what, on a quest."

"Hail," said Merlyn, in his most mysterious manner.

"Hail," replied the King, anxious to make a good impression.

They shook hands.

"Did you say Hail?" inquired the King, looking about him nervously. "I thought it was going to be fine, myself."

"He meant How-do-you-do," explained the Wart.

"Ah, yes, How-de-do?"

They shook hands again.

"Good afternoon," said King Pellinore. "What do you think the weather looks like now?"

"I think it looks like an anti-cyclone."

"Ah, yes," said the King. "An anti-cyclone. Well, I suppose I ought to be getting along."

At this the King trembled very much, opened and shut his visor several times, coughed, wove his reins into a knot, exclaimed, "I beg your pardon?" and showed signs of cantering away.

"He is a white magician," said the Wart. "You need not be afraid of him. He is my best friend, your majesty, and in any case he generally gets his spells muddled up."

"Ah, yes," said King Pellinore. "A white magician, what? How small the world is, is it not? How-de-do?"

"Hail," said Merlyn.

"Hail," said King Pellinore.

They shook hands for the third time.

"I should not go away," said the wizard, "if I were you. Sir Grummore Grummursum is on the way to challenge you to a joust."

"No, you don't say? Sir What-you-may-call-it coming here to challenge me to a joust?"

"Assuredly."

"Good handicap man?"

"I should think it would be an even match."

"Well, I must say," exclaimed the king, "it never hails but it pours."

"Hail," said Merlyn.

"Hail," said King Pellinore.

"Hail," said the Wart.

"Now I really won't shake hands with anybody else," announced the monarch. "We must assume that we have all met before."

"Is Sir Grummore really coming," inquired the Wart, hastily changing the subject, "to challenge King Pellinore to a battle?"

"Look yonder," said Merlyn, and both of them looked in the direction of his outstretched finger.

Sir Grummore Grummursum was cantering up the clearing in full panoply of war. Instead of his ordinary helmet with a visor he was wearing the proper tilting helm, which looked like a large coal-scuttle, and as he cantered he clanged.

He was singing his old school song:

We'll tilt together
Steady from crupper to poll,
And nothin' in life shall sever
Our love for the dear old coll.

Follow-up, follow-up, follow-up, follow-up, follow-up,
Till the shield ring again and again
With the clanks of the clanky true men.

"Goodness," exclaimed King Pellinore. "It's about two months since I had a proper tilt, and last winter they put me up to eighteeen. That was when they had the new handicaps."

Sir Grummore had arrived while he was speaking, and had recognized the Wart.

"Mornin'," said Sir Grummore. "You're Sir Ector's boy, ain't you? And who's that chap in the comic hat?"

"That is my tutor," said the Wart hurriedly. "Merlyn, the magician."

Sir Grummore looked at Merlyn — magicians were considered rather middle-class by the true jousting set in those days — and said distantly, "Ah, a magician. How-de-do?"

"And this is King Pellinore," said the Wart. "Sir Grummore Grummursum — King Pellinore."

"How-de-do?" inquired Sir Grummore.

"Hail," said King Pellinore. "No, I mean it won't hail, will it?"

"Nice day," said Sir Grummore.

"Yes, it is nice, isn't it, what?"

"Been questin' today?"

"Oh, yes, thank you. Always am questing, you know. After the Questing Beast."

"Interestin' job, that, very."

"Yes, it is interesting. Would you like to see some fewmets?"

"By Jove, yes. Like to see some fewmets."

"I have some better ones at home, but these are quite good, really."

"Bless my soul. So these are her fewmets."

"Yes, these are her fewmets."

"Interestin' fewmets."

"Yes, they are interesting, aren't they? Only you get tired of them," added King Pellinore.

"Well, well. It's a fine day, isn't it?"

"Yes, it is rather fine."

"Suppose we'd better have a joust, eh, what?"

"Yes, I suppose we had better," said King Pellinore, "really."

"What shall we have it for?"

"Oh, the usual, I suppose. Would one of you kindly help me on with my helm?"

They all three had to help him on eventually, for, what with the unscrewing of screws and the easing of nuts and bolts which the King had clumsily set on the wrong thread when getting up in a hurry that morning, it was quite a feat of engineering to get him out of his helmet and into his helm. The helm was an enormous thing like an oil drum, padded inside with two thicknesses of leather and three inches of straw.

As soon as they were ready, the two knights stationed themselves at each end of the clearing and then advanced to meet in the middle.

"Fair knight," said King Pellinore, "I pray thee tell me thy name."

"That me regards," replied Sir Grummore, using the proper formula.

"That is uncourteously said," said King Pellinore, "what? For no knight ne dreadeth for to speak his name openly, but for some reason of shame."

"Be that as it may, I choose that thou shalt not know my name as at this time, for no askin'."

"Then you must stay and joust with me, false knight."

"Haven't you got that wrong, Pellinore?" inquired Sir Grummore. "I believe it ought to be 'thou shalt'."

"Oh, I'm sorry, Sir Grummore. Yes, so it should, of course. Then thou shalt stay and joust with me, false knight."

Without further words, the gentlemen retreated to the opposite ends of the clearing, fewtered their spears, and prepared to hurtle together in the preliminary charge.

"I think we had better climb this tree," said Merlyn. "You never know what will happen in a joust like this."

They climbed up the big beech, which had easy branches sticking out in all directions, and the Wart stationed himself towards the end of a smooth bough about fifteen feet up, where he could get a good view. Nothing is so comfortable to sit in as a beech.]

To be able to picture the terrible battle which now took place, there is one thing which ought to be known. A knight in his full armour of those days, or at any rate during the heaviest days of armour, was generally carrying as much or more than his own weight in metal. He often weighed no less that twenty-two stone, and sometimes as much as twenty-five. This meant that his horse had to be a slow and enormous weight-carrier, like the farm horse of today, and that his own movements were so hampered by his burden of iron and padding that they were toned down into slow motion, as on the cinema.

"They're off!" cried the Wart, holding his breath with excitement.

Slowly and majestically, the ponderous horses lumbered into a walk. The spears, which had been pointing in the air, bowed to a horizontal line and pointed at each other. King Pellinore and Sir Grummore could be seen to be thumping their horses' sides with their heels for all they were worth, and in a few minutes the splendid animals had shambled into an earth-shaking imitation of a trot. Clank, rumble, thump-thump went the horses, and now the two knights were flapping their elbows and legs in unison, showing a good deal of daylight at their seats. There was a change in tempo, and Sir Grummore's horse could be definitely seen to be cantering. In another minute King Pellinore's was doing so too. It was a terrible spectacle.

"Oh, dear!" exclaimed the Wart, feeling ashamed that his blood-thirstiness had been responsible for making these two knights joust before him. "Do you think they will kill each other?"

"Dangerous sport," said Merlyn, shaking his head.

"Now!" cried the Wart.

With a blood-curdling beat of iron hoofs the mighty equestrians came together. Their spears wavered for a moment within a few inches of each other's helms — each had chosen the difficult point-stroke — and then they were galloping off in opposite directions. Sir Grummore drove his spear deep into the beech tree where they were sitting, and stopped dead. King Pellinore, who had been run away with, vanished altogether behind his back.

"Is it safe to look?" inquired the Wart, who had shut his eyes at the critical moment.

"Quite safe," said Merlyn. "I will take them some time to get back into position."

"Whoa, whoa, I say!" cried King Pellinore in muffled and distant tones, far away among the gorse bushes.

"Hi, Pellinore, hi!" shouted Sir Grummore. "Come back, my dear fellah, I'm over here."

There was a long pause, while the complicated stations of the two knights readjusted themselves, and then King Pellinore was at the opposite end from that at which he had started, while Sir Grummore faced him from his original position.

"Traitor knight!" cried Sir Grummore.

"Yield, recreant, what?" cried King Pellinore.

They fewtered their spears again, and thundered into the charge.

"Oh," said the Wart, "I hope they don't hurt themselves."

But the two mounts were patiently blundering together, and the two knights had simultaneously decided on the sweeping stroke. Each held his spear at right angles toward the left, and, before the Wart could say anything further, there was a terrific yet melodious thump. Clang! went the armour, like a motor omnibus in collision with a smithy, and the jousters were sitting side by side on the green sward, while their horses cantered off in opposite directions.

"A splendid fall," said Merlyn.

The two horses pulled themselves up, their duty done, and began resignedly to eat the sward. King Pellinore and Sir Grummore sat looking straight before them, each with the other's spear clasped hopefully under his arm.

"Well!" said the Wart. "What a bump! They both seem to be all right, so far."

Sir Grummore and King Pellinore laboriously got up,

"Defend thee," cried King Pellinore.

"God save thee," cried Sir Grummore.

With this they drew their swords and rushed together with such ferocity that each, after dealing the other a dent on the helm, sat down suddenly backwards.

"Bah!" cried King Pellinore,

"Booh!" cried Sir Grummore, also sitting down.

"Mercy," exclaimed the Wart. "What a combat!"

The knights had now lost their tempers and the battle was joined in earnest. It did not matter much, however, for they were so encased in metal that they could not do each other much damage. It took them so long to get up, and the dealing of a blow when you weighed the eighth part of a ton was such a cumbrous business, that every stage of the contest could be marked and pondered.

In the first stage King Pellinore and Sir Grummore stood opposite each other for about half an hour, and walloped each other on the helm. There was only opportunity for one blow at a time, so they more or less took it in turns, King Pellinore striking while Sir Grummore was recovering, and vice versa. At first, if either of them dropped his sword or got it stuck in the ground, the other put in two or three extra blows while he was patiently fumbling for it or trying to tug it out. Later, they fell into the rhythm of the thing more perfectly, like the toy mechanical people who saw wood on Christmas trees. Eventually the exercise and the monotony restored their good humour and they began to get bored.

The second stage was introduced as a change, by common consent. Sir Grummore stumped off to one end of the clearing, while King Pellinore plodded off to the other. Then they turned round and swayed backward and forward once or twice, in order to get their weight on their toes. When they leaned forward they had to run forward, to keep up with their weight, and if they leaned too far backward they fell down. So even walking was complicated. When they had got their weight properly distributed in front of them, so that they were just off their balance, each broke into a trot to keep up with himself. They hurtled together as it had been two boars.

They met in the middle, breast to breast, with a noise of shipwreck and great bells tolling, and both, bouncing off, fell breathless on their backs. They lay thus for a few minutes, panting. Then they slowly began to heave themselves to their feet, and it was obvious that they had lost their tempers once again.

King Pellinore had not only lost his temper, but he seemed to have been a bit astonished by the impact. He got up facing the wrong way, and could not find Sir Grummore. There was some excuse for this, since he had only a slit to peep through — and that was three inches away from his eye owing to the padding of straw — but he looked muddled as well. Perhaps he had broken his spectacles. Sir Grummore was quick to seize advantage.

"Take that!" cried Sir Grummore, giving the unfortunate monarch a two-handed swipe on the nob as he was slowly turning his head from side to side, peering in the opposite direction.

King Pellinore turned round morosely, but his opponent had been too quick for him. He had ambled round so that he was still behind the King, and now gave him another terrific blow in the same place.

"Where are you?" asked King Pellinore.

"Here," cried Sir Grummore, giving him another.

The poor king turned himself round as nimbly as possible, but Sir Grummore had given him the slip again.

"Tally-ho back!" shouted Sir Grummore, with another wallop.

"I think you're a *cad*," said the King.

"Wallop!" replied Sir Grummore, doing it.

What with the preliminary crash, the repeated blows on the back of his head, and the puzzling nature of his opponent, King Pellinore could now be seen to be visibly troubled in his brains. He swayed backward and forward under the hail of blows which were administered, and feebly wagged his arms.

"Poor King," said the Wart. "I wish he would not hit him so."

As if in answer to his wish, Sir Grummore paused in his labours.

"Do you want Pax?" asked Sir Grummore.

King Pellinore made no answer.

Sir Grummore favoured him with another whack and said, "If you don't say Pax, I shall cut your head off."

"I won't," said the King.

Whang! went the sword on top of his head.

Whang! it went again.

Whang! for the third time.

"Pax," said King Pellinore, mumbling rather.

Then, just as Sir Grummore was relaxing with the fruits of victory, he swung round upon him, shouted "Non!" at the top of his voice, and gave him a good push in the middle of the chest.

Sir Grummore fell over backwards.

"Well!" exclaimed the Wart. "What a cheat! I would not have thought it of him."

King Pellinore hurriedly sat on his victim's chest, thus increasing the weight upon him to a quarter of a ton and making it quite impossible for him to move, and began to undo Sir Grummore's helm.

"You said Pax!"

"I said Pax Non under my breath."

"It's a swindle."

"It's not."

"You're a cad."

"No, I'm not."

"Yes you are."

"No, I'm not."

"Yes, you are."

"I said Pax Non."

"You said Pax."

"No, I didn't."

"Yes, you did."

"No, I didn't."

"Yes, you did."

By this time Sir Grummore's helm was unlaced and they could see his bare head glaring at King Pellinore, quite purple in the face.

"Yield thee, recreant," said the King.

"Shan't," said Sir Grummore.

"You have got to yield, or I shall cut off your head."

"Cut it off then."

"Oh come on," said the King. "You know you have to yield when your helm is off."

"Feign I," said Sir Grummore.

"Well, I shall just cut your head off."

"I don't care."

The King waved his sword menacingly in the air.

"Go on," said Sir Grummore. "I dare you to."

The King lowered his sword and said, "Oh, I say, do yield, please."

"You yield," said Sir Grummore.

"But I can't yield. I am on top of you after all, am I not, what?"

"Well, I have feigned yieldin'."

"Oh, come on, Grummore. I do think you are a cad not to yield. You know very well I can't cut your head off."

"I would not yield to a cheat who started fightin' after he said Pax."

"I am not a cheat."

"You are a cheat."

"No, I'm not."

"Yes, you are."

"No, I'm not."

"Yes, you are."

"Very well," said King Pellinore. "You can jolly well get up and put on your helm and we will have a fight. I won't be called a cheat for anybody."

"Cheat!" said Sir Grummore.

They stood up and fumbled together with the helm, hissing, "No, I'm not" — "Yes, you are," until it was safely on. Then they retreated to opposite ends of the clearing, got their weight upon their toes, and came rumbling and thundering together like two runaway trains.

Unfortunately they were now so cross that they had both ceased to be vigilant, and in the fury of the moment they missed each other altogether. The momentum of their armour was too great for them to stop till they had passed each other handsomely, and then they manoeuvred about in such a manner that neither happened to come within the other's range of vision. It was funny watching them because King Pellinore, having already been caught from behind once, was continually spinning round to look behind him, and Sir Grummore, having used the stratagem himself, was doing the same thing. Thus they wandered for some five minutes, standing still, listening, clanking, crouching, creeping, peering, walking on tiptoe, and occasionally making a chance swipe behind their backs. Once they were standing within a few feet of each other, back to back, only to stalk off in opposite directions with infinite precaution, and once King Pellinore did hit Sir Grummore with one of his back strokes, but they both immediately spun round so often that they become giddy and mislaid each other afresh.

After five minutes, Sir Grummore said, "All right, Pellinore. It is no use hidin'. I can see where you are."

"I am not hiding," exclaimed King Pellinore indignantly. "Where am I?"

They discovered each other and went up close together, face to face.

"Cad," said Sir Grummore.

"Yah," said King Pellinore.

They turned round and marched off to their corners, seething with indignation.

"Swindler," shouted Sir Grummore.

"Beastly bully," shouted King Pellinore.

With this they summoned all their energies together for one decisive encounter, leaned forward, lowered their heads like two billy-goats, and positively sprinted together for the final blow. Alas, their aim was poor. They missed each other by about five yards, passed at full steam doing at least eight knots, like ships that pass in the night but speak not to each other in passing, and hurtled onward to their doom. Both knights began waving their arms like windmills, anti-clockwise, in the vain effort to slow up. Both continued with undiminished speed. Then Sir Grummore rammed his head against the beech in which the Wart was sitting, and King Pellinore collided with a chestnut at the other side of the clearing. The trees shook, the forest rang. Blackbirds and squirrels cursed and wood-pigeons flew out of their leafy perches half a mile away. The two knights stood to attention while one could count three. Then, with a last unanimous melodious clang, they both fell prostrate on the fatal sward.

["Stunned," said Merlyn, "I should think."

"Oh, dear," said the Wart. "Ought we to get down and help them?"

"We could pour water on their heads," said Merlyn reflectively, "if there was any water. But I don't suppose they would thank us for making their armour rusty. They will be all right. Besides, it is time that we were home."

"But they might be dead!"

"They are not dead, I know. In a minute or two they will come round and go off home to dinner."

D

"Poor King Pellinore has not got a home."

"Then Sir Grummore will invite him to stay the night. They will be the best of friends when they come to. They always are."

"Do you think so?"

"My dear boy, I know so. Shut your eyes and we will be off."

The Wart gave in to Merlyn's superior knowledge. "Do you think," he asked with his eyes shut, "that Sir Grummore has a feather bed?"

"Probably."

"Good," said the Wart. "That will be nice for King Pellinore, even if he was stunned."

The Latin words were spoken and the secret passes made. The funnel of whistling noise and space received them. In two seconds they were lying under the grandstand, and the sergeant's voice was calling from the opposite side of the tilting ground, "Nah then, Master Art, nah then. You've been a-snoozing there long enough. Come aht into the sunlight 'ere with Master Kay, one-two, one-two, and see some real tilting."]

THE CRICKET MATCH

from "England, their England"   **43**
by A.G. Macdonell   [33½]

Donald, a Scotsman, is anxious to see the famed English "team-spirit" in action.

["Don't forget Saturday morning Charing Cross Underground Station," ran the telegram which arrived at Royal Avenue during the week, "at ten fifteen sharp whatever you do dont be late Hodge."

Saturday morning was bright and sunny, and at ten minutes past 10 Donald arrived at the Embankment entrance of Charing Cross Underground Station, carrying a small suitcase full of clothes suitable for outdoor sports and pastimes. He was glad that he had arrived too early, for it would have been a dreadful thing for a stranger and a foreigner to have kept such a distinguished man, and his presumably distinguished colleagues, even for an instant from their national game. Laying his bag down on the pavement and putting one foot upon it carefully — for Donald had heard stories of the surpassing dexterity of metropolitan thieves — he waited eagerly for the hands of a neighbouring clock to mark the quarter-past. At twenty minutes to 11 an effeminate-looking young man, carrying a cricket bag and wearing a pale-blue silk jumper up to his ears, sauntered up, remarked casually, "You playing?" and, receiving an answer in the affirmative, dumped his bag at Donald's feet and said, "Keep an eye on that like a good fellow. I'm going to get a shave," and sauntered off round the corner.

At five minutes to 11 there was a respectable muster, six of the team having assembled. But at five minutes past, a disintegrating element was introduced by the arrival of Mr. Harcourt with the news, which he announced with the air of a shipwrecked mariner who has, after twenty-five years of vigilance, seen a sail, that in the neighbourhood of Charing Cross the pubs opened at 11 a.m. So that when Mr. Hodge himself turned up at twenty-five minutes past 11, resplendent in flannels, a red-and-white football shirt with a lace-up collar, and a blazer of purple-and-yellow stripes, each stripe being at least two inches across, and surmounted by a purple-and-yellow cap that made him somehow reminiscent of one of the Michelin twins, if not both, he was justly indignant at the slackness of his team.

"They've no sense of time," he told Donald repeatedly. "We're late as it is. The match is due to begin at half-past 11, and it's fifty miles from here. I should have been here myself two hours ago but I had my Sunday article to do. It really is too bad."

When the team, now numbering nine men, had been extricated from the tavern and had been marshalled on the pavement, counted, recounted, and the missing pair identified, it was pointed out by the casual youth who had returned, shining and pomaded from the barber, that the char-a-banc had not yet arrived.

Mr. Hodge's indignation became positively alarming and he covered the twenty yards to the public telephone box almost as quickly as Mr. Harcourt covered the forty yards back to the door of the pub. Donald remained on the pavement to guard the heap of suitcases, cricket-bags, and stray equipment — one player had arrived with a pair of flannels rolled in a tight ball under his arm and a left-hand batting glove, while another had contributed a cardboard box which he had bought at Hamley's on the way down, and which contained six composite cricket-balls, boys' size, and a pair of bails. It was just as well Donald did remain on guard, partly because no one else seemed to care whether the luggage was stolen or not, partly because Mr. Hodge emerged in a perfect frenzy a minute or two later from the telephone box to borrow two pennies to put in the slot, and partly because by the time the telephone call was at last in full swing and Mr. Hodge's command over the byways of British invective was enjoying complete freedom of action, the char-a-banc rolled up beside the kerb.

At 12.30 it was decided not to wait for the missing pair, and the nine cricketers started off. At 2.30, after halts at Catford, the White Hart at Sevenoaks, the Angel at Tunbridge Wells, and three smaller inns at tiny villages, the char-a-banc drew up triumphantly beside the cricket ground of the Kentish village of Fordenden.

Donald was enchanted at his first sight of rural England. And rural England is the real England, unspoilt by factories and financiers and tourists and hustle. He sprang out of the char-a-banc, in which he had been tightly wedged between a very stout publisher who had laughed all the way down and had quivered at each laugh like the needle of a seismograph during one of Japan's larger earthquakes and a youngish and extremely learned professor of ballistics, and gazed eagerly round. The sight was worth an eager gaze or two. It was a hot summer's afternoon. There was no wind, and the smoke from the red-roofed cottages curled slowly up into the golden haze. The clock on the flint tower of the church struck the half-hour, and the vibrations spread slowly across the shimmering hedgerows, spangled with white blossom of the convolvulus, and lost themselves tremulously among the orchards. Bees lazily drifted. White butterflies flapped their aimless way among the gardens. Dephiniums, lark-spur, tiger-lilies, evening primrose, monk's-hood, sweet-peas, swaggered brilliantly above the box hedges, the wooden palings, and the rickety gates. The cricket field itself was a mass of daisies and buttercups and dandelions, tall grasses and purple vetches and thistle-down, and great clumps of dark-red sorrel, except, of course, for the oblong patch in the centre — mown, rolled, watered — a smooth, shining emerald of grass, the Pride of Fordenden, the Wicket.

The entire scene was perfect to the last detail. It was as if Mr. Cochran had, with his spectacular genius, brought Ye Olde Englyshe Village straight down by special train from the London Pavilion, complete with synthetic cobwebs (from the Wigan factory), hand-made smocks for ye gaffers (called in the cabaret scenes and the North-West Mounted Police scenes, the Gentlemen of the Singing Ensemble), and aluminium Eezi-Milk stools for the dairymaids (or Ladies of the Dancing Ensemble). For there stood the Vicar, beaming absentmindedly at everyone. There was the forge, with the blacksmith, his hammer discarded, tightening his snake-buckled belt for the fray and loosening his braces to enable his terrific bowling-arm to swing freely in its socket. There on a long bench outside the Three Horseshoes sat a row of elderly men, facing a row of pint tankards, and wearing either long beards or clean-shaven chins and long whiskers. Near them holding pint tankards in their hands, was another group of men, clustered together and talking with intense animation. Donald thought that one or two of them seemed familiar, but it was not until he turned back to the char-a-banc to ask if he could help with the luggage that he realized that they were Mr. Hodge and his team already sampling the proprietor's wares. (A notice above the door of the inn stated that the proprietor's name was A. Bason and that he was licensed to sell wines, spirits, beers, and tobacco.)

All round the cricket field small parties of villagers were patiently waiting for the great match to begin – a match against gentlemen from London is an event in a village – and some of them looked as if they had been waiting for a good long time. But they were not impatient. Village folk are very seldom impatient. Those whose lives are occupied in combating the eccentricities of God regard as very small beer the eccentricities of Man.

Blue-and-green dragonflies played at hide-and-seek among the thistle-down and a pair of swans flew overhead. An ancient man leaned upon a scythe, his sharpening-stone sticking out of a pocket in his velveteen waistcoat. A magpie flapped lazily across the meadows. The parson shook hands with the squire. Doves cooed. The haze flickered. The world stood still.]

At twenty minutes to 3, Mr. Hodge had completed his rather tricky negotiations with the Fordenden captain, and had arranged that two substitutes should be lent by Fordenden in order that the visitors should field eleven men, and that nine men on each side should bat. But just as the two men on the Fordenden side, who had been detailed for the unpleasant duty of fielding for both sides and batting for neither, had gone off home in high dudgeon, a motor-car arrived containing not only Mr. Hodge's two defaulters but a third gentleman in flannels as well, who swore stoutly that he had been invited by Mr. Hodge to play and affirmed that he was jolly well going to play. Whoever stood down, it wasn't going to be him. Negotiations therefore had to be reopened, the pair of local Achilles had to be recalled, and at ten minutes to 3 the match began upon a twelve-a-side basis.

Mr. Hodge, having won the toss by a system of his own founded upon the differential calculus and the Copernican theory, sent in his opening pair to bat. One was James Livingstone, a very sound club cricketer, and the other one was called, simply, Boone. Boone was a huge, awe-inspiring colossus of a man, weighing at least eighteen stone and wearing all the majestic trappings of a Cambridge Blue. Donald felt that it was hardly fair to loose such cracks upon a humble English village until he fortunately remembered that he, of all people, a foreigner, admitted by courtesy to the National Game, ought not to set himself up to be a judge of what is, and what is not, cricket.

The Fordenden team ranged themselves at the bidding of their captain, the Fordenden baker, in various spots of vantage amid the daisies, buttercups, dandelions, vetches, thistle-down, and clumps of dark-red sorrel; and the blacksmith having taken in, just for luck as it were, yet another reef in his snake-buckle belt, prepared to open the attack. It so happened that, at the end at which he was to bowl, the ground behind the wicket was level for a few yards and then sloped away rather abruptly, so that it was only during the last three or four intensive, galvanic yards of his run that the blacksmith, who took a long run, was visible to the batsman or indeed to anyone on the field of play except the man stationed in the deep field behind him. This man saw nothing of the game except the blacksmith walking back dourly and the blacksmith running up ferociously, and occasionally a ball driven smartly over the brow of the hill in his direction.

The sound club player having taken guard, having twiddled his bat round several times in a nonchalant manner, and having stared arrogantly at each fieldsman in turn, was somewhat surprised to find that, although the field was ready, no bowler was visible. His doubts, however, were resolved a second or two later, when the blacksmith came up, breasting the slope superbly [like a mettlesome combination of Vulcan and Venus Anadyomene]. The first ball which he delivered was a high full-pitch to leg, of appalling velocity. It must have lighted upon a bare patch among the long grass near long-leg, for it rocketed, first bounce, into the hedge and four byes were reluctantly signalled by the village umpire. The row of gaffers on the rustic bench shook their heads, agreed that it was many years since four byes had been signalled on that ground, and called for more pints of old-and-mild. The other members of Mr. Hodge's team blanched visibly and called for more pints of bitter. The youngish professor of ballistics, who was in next, muttered something about muzzle velocities and started to do a sum on the back on an envelope.

The second ball went full-pitch into the wicket-keeper's stomach and there was a delay while the deputy wicket-keeper was invested with the pads and glove of office. The third ball, making a noise like a partridge, would have hummed past Mr. Livingstone's left ear had he not dexterously struck it out of the ground for six, and the fourth took his leg bail with a bullet-like full-pitch. Ten runs for one wicket, last man six. The professor got the fifth ball on the left ear and went back to the Three Horseshoes, while Mr. Harcourt had the singular misfortune to hit his wicket before the sixth ball was even delivered. Ten runs for two wickets and one man retired hurt. A slow left-hand bowler was on at the other end, the local rate-collector, a man whose whole life was one of infinite patience and guile. Off his first ball the massive Cambridge Blue was easily stumped, having executed a movement that aroused the professional admiration of the Ancient who was leaning upon his scythe. Donald was puzzled that so famous a player should play so execrable a stroke until it transpired, later on, that a wrong impression had been created and that the portentous Boone had gained his Blue at Cambridge for rowing and not for cricket. Ten runs for three wickets and one man hurt.

The next player was a singular young man. He was small and quiet, and he wore perfectly creased white flannels, white silk socks, a pale-pink silk shirt, and a white cap. On the way down in the char-a-banc he had taken little part in the conversation and even less in the beer-drinking. [There was a retiring modesty about him that made him conspicuous in that cricket eleven, and there was a gentleness, an almost finicky gentleness about his movements which hardly seemed virile and athletic.] He looked as if a fast ball would knock the bat out of his hands. Donald asked someone what his name was, and was astonished to learn that he was the famous novelist, Robert Southcott himself.

Just as this celebrity, holding his bat as delicately as if it was a flute or fan, was picking his way through the daisies and thistle-down towards the wicket, Mr. Hodge rushed anxiously, tankard in hand, from the Three Horseshoes and bellowed in a most unpoetical voice: "Play carefully, Bobby. Keep your end up. Runs don't matter."

"Very well, Bill," replied Mr. Southcott sedately. Donald was interested by this little exchange. It was the Team Spirit at work — the captain instructing his man to play a type of game that was demanded by the state of the team's fortunes, and the individual loyally suppressing his instincts to play a different type of game.

Mr. Southcott took guard modestly, glanced furtively round the field as if it was an impertinence to suggest that he would survive long enough to make a study of the fieldsmen's positions worth while, and hit the rate-collector's first ball over the Three Horseshoes into a hay-field. The ball was retrieved by a mob of screaming urchins, handed back to the rate-collector, who scratched his head and then bowled his fast yorker, which Mr. Southcott hit into the saloon bar of the Shoes, giving Mr. Harcourt such a fright that he required several pints before he fully recovered his nerve. The next ball was very slow and crafty, endowed as it was with every iota of finger-spin and brain-power which a long-service rate-collector could muster. In addition, it was delivered at the extreme end of the crease so as to secure a background of dark laurels instead of a dazzling white screen, and it swung a little in the air; a few moments later the urchins, by this time delirious with ecstasy, were fishing it out of the squire's trout stream with a bamboo pole and an old bucket.

The rate-collector was bewildered. He had never known such a travesty of the game. It was not cricket. It was slogging; it was wild, unscientific bashing; and furthermore, his reputation was in grave danger. The instalments would be harder than ever to collect, and Heaven knew they were hard enough to collect as it was, what with bad times and all. His three famous deliveries had been treated with contempt — the leg-break, the fast yorker, and the slow, swinging off-break out of the laurel bushes. What on earth was he to try now? Another six and he would be laughed out of the parish. Fortunately the village umpire came out of a trance of consternation to the rescue. Thirty-eight years of umpiring for the Fordenden Cricket Club had taught him a thing or two and he called "Over" firmly and marched off to square-leg. The rate-collector was glad to give way to a Free Forester, who had been specially imported for this match. He was only a moderate bowler, but it was felt that it was worth while giving him a trial, if only for the sake of the scarf round his waist and his cap. At the other end the fast bowler pounded away grimly until an unfortunate accident occurred. Mr. Southcott had been treating with apologetic contempt those of his deliveries which came within reach, and the blacksmith's temper had been rising for some time. An urchin had shouted, "Take him off!" and the other urchins, for whom Mr. Southcott was by now a firmly established deity, had screamed with delight. The captain had held one or two ominous consultations with the wicket-keeper and other advisers, and the blacksmith knew that his dismissal was at hand unless he produced a supreme effort.

It was the last ball of the over. He halted at the wicket before going back for his run, glared at Mr. Harcourt, who had been driven out to umpire by his colleagues — greatly to the regret of Mr. Bason, the landlord of the Shoes —

glared at Mr. Southcott, took another reef in his belt, shook out another inch in his braces, spat on his hand, swung his arm three or four times in a meditative sort of way, grasped the ball tightly in his colossal palm, and then turned smartly about and marched off like a Pomeranian grenadier and vanished over the brow of the hill. Mr. Southcott, during these proceedings, leant elegantly upon his bat and admired the view. At last, after a long stillness, the ground shook, the grasses waved violently, small birds arose with shrill clamours, a loud puffing sound alarmed the butterflies, and the blacksmith, [looking more like Venus Anadyomene than ever,] came thundering over the crest. The world held its breath. Among the spectators conversation was suddenly hushed. Even the urchins, understanding somehow that they were assisting at a crisis in affairs, were silent for a moment as the mighty figure swept up to the crease. [It was the charge of Von Bredow's Dragoons at Gravelotte over again.]

But alas for human ambitions! Mr. Harcourt, swaying slightly from leg to leg, had understood the menacing glare of the bowler, had marked the preparation for a titanic effort, and − for he was not a poet for nothing − knew exactly what was going on. And Mr. Harcourt sober had a very pleasant sense of humour, but Mr. Harcourt rather drunk was a perfect demon of impishness. Sober, he occasionally resisted a temptation to try to be funny. Rather drunk, never. As the giant whirlwind of vulcanic energy rushed past him to the crease, Mr. Harcourt, quivering with excitement and internal laughter, and wobbling uncertainly upon his pins, took a deep breath and bellowed, "No ball!"

It was too late for the unfortunate bowler to stop himself. The ball flew out of his hand like a bullet and hit third-slip, who was not looking, full pitch on the knee-cap. With a yell of agony third-slip began hopping about like a stork until he tripped over a tussock of grass and fell on his face in a bed of nettles, from which he sprang up again with another drum-splitting yell. The blacksmith himself was flung forward by his own irresistible momentum, startled out of his wits by Mr. Harcourt's bellow in his ear, and thrown off his balance by his desperate effort to prevent himself from delivering the ball, and the result was that his gigantic feet got mixed up among each other and he fell heavily in the centre of the wicket, knocking up a cloud of dust and dandelion-seed and twisting his ankle. Rooks by hundreds arose in protest from the vicarage cedars. The urchins howled [like intoxicated banshees]. The gaffers gaped. Mr. Southcott gazed modestly at the ground. Mr. Harcourt gazed at the heavens. Mr. Harcourt did not think the world had ever been, or

could ever be again, quite such a capital place, even though he had laughed
internally so much that he had got hiccups.

Mr. Hodge, emerging at that moment from the Three Horseshoes, surveyed
the scene and then the scoreboard with an imperial air. Then he roared in the
same rustic voice as before:

"You needn't play safe any more, Bob. Play your own game."

"Thank you, Bill," replied Mr. Southcott as sedately as ever, and, on the
resumption of the game, he fell into a kind of cricketing trance, defending his
wicket skilfully from straight balls, ignoring crooked ones, and scoring one
more run in a quarter of an hour before he inadvertently allowed, for the first
time during his innings, a ball to strike his person.

"Out!" shrieked the venerable umpire before anyone had time to appeal.

The score at this point was sixty-nine for six, last man fifty-two.

The only other incident in the innings was provided by an American
journalist, by name Shakespeare Pollock — an intensely active, alert,
on-the-spot young man. Mr. Pollock had been roped in at the last moment to
make up the eleven, and Mr. Hodge and Mr. Harcourt had spent quite a lot of
time on the way down trying to teach him the fundamental principles of the
game. [Donald had listened attentively and had been surprised that they
made no reference to the Team Spirit. He decided in the end that the reason
must have been simply that everyone knows all about it already, and that it is
therefore taken for granted.]

Mr. Pollock stepped up to the wicket in the lively manner of his native
mustang, refused to take guard, on the ground that he wouldn't know what
to do with it when he had got it, and, striking the first ball he received
towards square leg, threw down his bat, and himself set off at a great rate in
the direction of cover-point. There was a paralysed silence. The rustics on the
bench rubbed their eyes. On the field no one moved. Mr. Pollock stopped
suddenly, looked round, and broke into a genial laugh.

"Darn me —" he began, and then he pulled himself up and went on in
refined English, "Well, well! I thought I was playing baseball." He smiled
disarmingly round.

"Baseball is a kind of rounders, isn't it, sir?" said cover-point sym-
pathetically.

Donald thought he had never seen an expression change so suddenly as Mr.
Pollock's did at this harmless, and true, statement. A look of concentrated,
ferocious venom obliterated the disarming smile. Cover-point, simple soul,
noticed nothing, however, and Mr. Pollock walked back to the wicket in

silence and was out next ball.

The next two batsmen, Major Hawker, the team's fast bowler, and Mr. Hodge himself, did not score, and the innings closed at sixty-nine, Donald not-out nought. Opinion on the gaffers' bench, which corresponded in years and connoisseur-ship very closely with the Pavilion at Lord's, was sharply divided on the question whether sixty-nine was, or was not, a winning score.

After a suitable interval for refreshment, Mr. Hodge led his men, except Mr. Harcourt who was missing, out into the field and placed them at suitable positions in the hay.

The batsmen came in. The redoubtable Major Hawker, the fast bowler, thrust out his chin and prepared to bowl. In a quarter of an hour he had terrified seven batsmen, clean bowled six of them, and broken a stump. Eleven runs, six wickets, last man two.

After the fall of the sixth wicket there was a slight delay. The new batsman, the local rate-collector, had arrived at the crease and was ready. But nothing happened. Suddenly the large publisher, who was acting as wicket-keeper, called out, "Hi! Where's Hawker?"

The words galvanized Mr. Hodge into portentous activity.

"Quick!" he shouted. "Hurry, run, for God's sake! Bob, George, Percy, to the Shoes!" and he set off at a sort of gallop toward the inn, followed at intervals by the rest of the side except the pretty youth in the blue jumper, who lay down; the wicket-keeper, who did not move; and Mr. Shakespeare Pollock, who had shot off the mark and was well ahead of the field.

But they were all too late, even Mr. Pollock. The gallant Major, admitted by Mr. Bason through the back door, had already lowered a quart and a half of mild-and-bitter, and his subsequent bowling was perfectly innocuous, consisting, as it did, mainly of slow, gentle full-pitches to leg which the village baker and even, occasionally, the rate-collector hit hard and high into the long grass. The score mounted steadily.

Disaster followed disaster. Mr. Pollock, presented with an easy chance of a run-out, instead of lobbing the ball back to the wicket-keeper, had another reversion to his college days and flung it with appalling velocity at the unfortunate rate-collector and hit him in the small of the back, shouting triumphantly as he did so, "Rah, rah, rah!" Mr. Livingstone, good club player, missed two easy catches off successive balls. Mr. Hodge allowed another easy catch to fall at his feet without attempting to catch it, and explained afterwards that he had been all the time admiring a particularly fine specimen of oak in the squire's garden. He seemed to think that this was a complete justification of his failure to attempt, let alone bring off, the catch. A black spot happened to cross the eye of the ancient umpire just as the baker put all his feet and legs and pads in front of a perfectly straight ball, and, as he plaintively remarked over and over again, he had to give the batsman the benefit of the doubt, hadn't he? It wasn't as if it was his fault that a black spot had crossed his eye just at that moment. And the stout publisher seemed to be suffering from the delusion that the way to make a catch at the wicket was to raise both hands high in the air, utter a piercing yell, and trust to an immense pair of pads to secure the ball. Repeated experiments proved that he was wrong.

The baker lashed away vigorously and the rate-collector dabbed the ball hither and thither until the score — having once been eleven runs for six wickets — was marked up on the board at fifty runs for six wickets. Things were desperate. Twenty to win and five wickets — assuming that the blacksmith's ankle and third-slip's knee-cap would stand the strain — to fall. If the lines on Mr. Hodge's face were deep, the lines on the faces of his team when he put himself on to bowl were like plasticine models of the Colorado Canyon. Mr. Southcott, without any orders from his captain, discarded his silk sweater from the Rue de la Paix, and went away into the deep field, about a hundred and twenty yards from the wicket. His beautifully brushed head was hardly visible above the daisies. The professor of ballistics sighed deeply. Major Hawker grinned a colossal grin, right across his jolly red face, and edged off in the direction of the Shoes. Livingstone, loyal to his captain, crouched alertly. Mr. Shakespeare Pollock rushed about enthusiastically. The remainder of the team drooped.

But the remainder of the team was wrong. For a wicket, a crucial wicket, was secured off Mr. Hodge's very first ball. It happened like this. Mr. Hodge was a poet, and therefore a theorist, and an idealist. If he was to win a victory at anything, he preferred to win by brains and not by muscle. He would far sooner have his best leg-spinner miss the wicket by an eighth of an inch than dismiss a batsman with a fast, clumsy full-toss. Every ball that he bowled had brain behind it, if not exactness of pitch. And it so happened that he had recently watched a country cricket match between Lancashire [a county that he detested in theory,] and Worcestershire, [a county that he adored in fact. On the one side were factories and the late Mr. Jimmy White; on the other, English apples and Mr. Stanley Baldwin.] And at this particular match, a Worcestershire bowler, by name Root, a deliciously agricultural name, had outed the tough nuts of the County Palatine by placing all his fieldsmen on the leg-side and bowling what are technically known as 'in-swingers'.

Mr. Hodge, [at heart an agrarian, for all his book-learning and his cadences,] was determined to do the same. The first part of the performance was easy. He placed all his men upon the leg-side. The second part — the bowling of the 'in-swingers' — was more complicated, and Mr. Hodge's first ball was a slow long-hop on the off-side. The rate-collector, metaphorically rubbing his eyes, felt that this was too good to be true, and he struck the ball sharply into the untenanted off-side and ambled down the wicket with as near an approach to gaiety as a man can achieve who is cut off by the very nature of his profession from the companionship and goodwill of his fellows. He had hardly gone a yard or two when he was paralysed by a hideous yell from the long grass into which the ball had vanished, and still more by the sight of Mr. Harcourt, who, aroused from a deep slumber amid a comfortable couch of grasses and daisies, sprang to his feet and, pulling himself together with miraculous rapidity after a lightning if somewhat bleary glance round the field, seized the ball and unerringly threw down the wicket. Fifty for seven, last man twenty-two. Twenty to win: four wickets to fall.

Mr. Hodge's next ball was his top-spinner, and it would have, or might have, come very quickly off the ground had it ever hit the ground; as it was, one of the short-legs caught it dexterously and threw it back while the umpire signalled a wide. Mr. Hodge then tried some more of Mr. Root's stuff and was promptly hit for two sixes and a single. This brought the redoubtable baker to the batting end. Six runs to win and four wickets to fall.

Mr. Hodge's fifth ball was not a good one, due mainly to the fact that it slipped out of his hand before he was ready, and it went up and came down in a slow, lazy parabola, about seven feet wide of the wicket on the leg-side. The baker had plenty of time to make up his mind. He could either leave it alone and let it count one run as a wide; or he could spring upon it like a panther and, with a terrific six, finish the match sensationally. [He could play the part either of a Quintus Fabius Maximus Cunctator, or of a sort of Tarzan. The baker concealed beneath a modest and floury exterior a mounting ambition.] Here was his chance to show the village. He [chose the sort of Tarzan,] sprang like a panther, whirled his bat cyclonically, and missed the ball by about a foot and a half. The wicket-keeping publisher had also had time in which to think and to move, and he also had covered the seven feet. True, his movements were less like the spring of a panther than the sideways waddle of an aldermanic penguin. But nevertheless he got there, and when the ball had passed the flashing blade of the baker, he launched a mighty kick at it – stooping to grab it was out of the question – and by an amazing fluke kicked it on to the wicket. Even the ancient umpire had to give the baker out, for the baker was still lying flat on his face outside the crease.

"I was bowling for that," observed Mr. Hodge modestly, strolling up the pitch.

"I had plenty of time to use my hands," remarked the wicket-keeper to the world at large, "but I preferred to kick it."

Donald was impressed by the extraordinary subtlety of the game.

Six to win and three wickets to fall.

The next batsman was a schoolboy of about sixteen, an ingenuous youth with pink cheeks and a nervous smile, who quickly fell a victim to Mr. Harcourt, now wideawake and beaming upon everyone. For Mr. Harcourt, poet that he was, understood exactly what the poor, pink child was feeling, and he knew that if he played the ancient dodge and pretended to lose the ball in the long grass, it was a hundred to one that the lad would lose his head. The batsman at the other end played the fourth ball of Mr. Livingstone's next over hard in the direction of Mr. Harcourt. Mr. Harcourt rushed towards the spot where it had vanished in the jungle. He groped wildly for it, shouting as he did so, "Come and help. It's lost." The pink child scuttered nimbly down the pitch. Six runs to win and two wickets to fall. Mr. Harcourt smiled demoniacally.

The crisis was now desperate. The fieldsmen drew nearer and nearer to the batsmen, excepting the youth in the blue jumper. Livingstone balanced himself on his toes. Mr. Shakespeare Pollock hopped about almost on top of the batsmen, and breathed excitedly and audibly. Even the imperturbable Mr. Southcott discarded the piece of grass which he had been chewing so steadily. Mr. Hodge took himself off and put on the Major, who had by now somewhat lived down the quart and a half.

The batsmen crouched down upon their bats and defended stubbornly. A snick through the slips brought a single. A ball which eluded the publisher's gigantic pads brought a bye. A desperate sweep at a straight half-volley sent the ball off the edge of the bat over third-man's head and in normal circumstances would have certainly scored one, and possibly two. But Mr. Harcourt was on guard at third-man, and the batsmen, by nature cautious men, one being old and the sexton, the other the postman and therefore a Government official, were taking no risks. Then came another single off a mis-hit, and then an interminable period in which no wicket fell and no run was scored. It was broken at last disastrously, for the postman struck the ball sharply at Mr. Pollock, and Mr. Pollock picked it up and, in an ecstasy of zeal. flung it madly at the wicket. Two overthrows resulted.

The scores were level and there were two wickets to fall. Silence fell. The gaffers, victims simultaneously of excitement and senility, could hardly raise their pint pots — for it was past 6 o'clock, and the front door of the Three Horseshoes was now as wide open officially as the back door had been unofficially all afternoon.

The Major, his red face redder than ever [and his chin sticking out almost as far as the Napoleonic Mr. Ogilvy's,] bowled a fast half-volley on the leg-stump. The sexton, a man of iron muscle from much digging, hit it fair and square in the middle of the bat, and it flashed like a thunderbolt, waist-high, straight at the youth in the blue jumper. With a shrill scream the youth sprang backwards out of its way and fell over on his back. Immediately behind him, so close were the fieldsmen clustered, stood the mighty Boone. There was no chance of escape for him. Even if he had possessed the figure and the agility to perform back-somersaults, he would have lacked the time. He had been unsighted by the youth in the jumper. The thunderbolt struck him in the midriff like a red hot cannon-ball upon a Spanish galleon, and with the sound of a drumstick upon an insufficiently stretched drum. With a fearful oath, Boone clapped his hands to his outraged stomach and found that the ball was in the way. He looked at it for a moment in astonishment and then threw it down angrily and started to massage the injured spot while the field rang with applause at the brilliance of the catch.

Donald walked up and shyly added his congratulations. Boone scowled at him.

"I didn't want to catch the bloody thing," he said sourly, massaging away like mad.

"But it may save the side," ventured Donald.

"Blast the bloody side," said Boone.

Donald went back to his place.

The scores were level and there was one wicket to fall. The last man in was the blacksmith, leaning heavily upon the shoulder of the baker, who was going to run for him, and limping as if in great pain. He took guard and looked round savagely. He was clearly still in a great rage.

The first ball he received he lashed at wildly and hit straight up in the air to an enormous height. It went up and up and up, until it became difficult to focus it properly against the deep, cloudless blue of the sky, and it carried with it the hopes and fears of an English village. Up and up it went and then at the top it seemed to hang motionless in the air, poised like a hawk, fighting, as it were, a heroic but forlorn battle against the chief invention of Sir Isaac Newton, and then it began its slow descent.

In the meanwhile things were happening below, on the terrestrial sphere. [Indeed, the situation was rapidly becoming what the French call *mouvementé*.] In the first place, the blacksmith forgot his sprained ankle and set out at a capital rate for the other end, roaring in a great voice as he went, "Come on, Joe!" The baker, who was running on behalf of the invalid, also set out, and he also roared "Come on, Joe!" and side by side, like a pair of high-stepping hackneys, the pair cantered along. From the other end Joe set out on his mission, and he roared "Come on, Bill!" So all three came on. And everything would have been all right, so far as the running was concerned, had it not been for the fact that Joe, very naturally, ran with his head thrown back and his eyes goggling at the hawk-like cricket-ball. And this in itself would not have mattered if it had not been for the fact that the blacksmith and the baker, also very naturally, ran with their heads turned not only upwards but also backwards as well, so that they too gazed at the ball, with an alarming sort of squint and a truly terrific kink in their necks. Half-way down the pitch the three met with a magnificent clang, reminiscent of early, happy days in the tournament-ring at Ashby-de-la-Zouche, and the hopes of the village fell with the resounding fall of their three champions.

But what of the fielding side? Things were not so well with them. If there was doubt and confusion among the warriors of Fordenden, there was also uncertainty and disorganization among the ranks of the invaders. Their main trouble was the excessive concentration of their forces in the neighbourhood of the wicket. Napoleon laid it down that it was impossible to have too many men upon a battlefield, and he used to do everything in his power to call up every available man for a battle. Mr. Hodge, after a swift glance at the ascending ball and a swift glance at the disposition of his troops, disagreed profoundly with the Emperor's dictum. He had too many men, far too many. And all except the youth in the blue silk jumper, and the mighty Boone, were moving towards strategical positions underneath the ball, and not one of them appeared to be aware that any of the others existed. Boone had not moved because he was more or less in the right place, but then Boone was not likely to bring off the catch, especially after the episode of the last ball. Major Hawker, shouting "Mine, mine!" in a magnificently self-confident voice, was coming up from the bowler's end like a battle-cruiser. Mr. Harcourt had obviously lost sight of the ball altogether, if indeed he had ever seen it, for he was running round and round Boone and giggling foolishly. Livingstone and Southcott, the two cracks, were approaching competently. Either of them would catch it easily. Mr. Hodge had only to choose between them and, coming to a swift decision, he yelled above the din, "Yours, Livingstone!" Southcott, disciplined cricketer, stopped dead. Then Mr. Hodge made a fatal mistake. He remembered Livingstone's two missed sitters, and he reversed his decision and roared "Yours, Bobby!" Mr. Southcott obediently started again, while Livingstone, who had not heard the second order, went straight on. Captain Hodge had restored the *status quo.*

In the meantime the professor of ballistics had made a lightning calculation of angles, velocities, density of the air, barometer-readings and temperatures, and had arrived at the conclusion that the critical point, the spot which ought to be marked in the photographs with an X, was one yard to the north-east of Boone, and he proceeded to take up station there, colliding on the way with Donald and knocking him over. A moment later Bobby Southcott came racing up and tripped over the recumbent Donald and was shot head first into the Abraham-like bosom of Boone. Boone stepped back a yard under the impact and came down with his spiked boot, surmounted by a good eighteen stone of flesh and blood, upon the professor's toe. Almost simultaneously the portly wicket-keeper, whose movements were a positive triumph of the spirit over the body, bumped the professor from behind. The learned man was thus neatly sandwiched between Tweedledum and Tweedledee, and the sandwich was instantly converted into a ragout by Livingstone, who made up for his lack of extra weight — for he was always in perfect training — by his extra momentum. And all the time Mr. Shakespeare Pollock hovered alertly upon the outskirts like a Rugby scrum-half, screaming American University cries in a piercingly high tenor voice.

At last the ball came down. To Mr. Hodge, it seemed a long time before the invention of Sir Isaac Newton finally triumphed. And it was a striking testimony to the mathematical and ballistical skill of the professor that the ball landed with a sharp report upon the top of his head. Thence it leapt up into the air a foot or so, cannoned on to Boone's head, and then trickled slowly down the colossal expanse of the wicket-keeper's back, bouncing slightly as it reached the massive lower portions. It was only a foot from the ground when Mr. Shakespeare Pollock sprang into the vortex with a last ear-splitting howl of victory and grabbed it off the seat of the wicket-keeper's trousers. The match was a tie. And hardly anyone on the field knew it except Mr. Hodge, the youth in the blue jumper, and Mr. Pollock himself. For the two batsmen and the runner, undaunted to the last, had picked themselves up and were bent on completing the single that was to give Fordenden the crown of victory. Unfortunately, dazed with their falls, with excitement, and with the noise, they all three ran for the same wicket, simultaneously realized their error, and all three turned and ran for the other — the blacksmith, ankle and all, in the centre and leading by a yard, [so that they looked like pictures of the Russian *troika*]. But their effort was in vain, for Mr. Pollock had grabbed the ball and the match was a tie.

[And both teams spent the evening at the Three Horseshoes, and Mr. Harcourt made a speech in Italian about the glories of England and afterwards fell asleep in a corner, and Donald got home to Royal Avenue at 1 o'clock in the morning, feeling that he had not learnt very much about the English from his experience of their national game.]

● *His favourite text was held to be:*
I Timothy 5, 23.

EXCITING

THE DEATH CART

from "A Journal of the Plague Year"
by Daniel Defoe

The Plague of London – 1665

John Hayward was at that time under-sexton of the parish of St Stephen, Coleman Street. This man went with the dead-cart and the bell to fetch the dead bodies from the houses where they lay, and fetched many of them out of the chambers and houses; which work he performed and never had the distemper at all, but lived about twenty years after it, and was sexton of the parish to the time of his death.

It was under this John Hayward's care, and within his bounds, that the story of the piper happened, and he assured me that it was true. It is said that it was a blind piper but, as John told me, the fellow was not blind, but an ignorant, weak, poor man, and usually walked his rounds about ten o'clock at night and went piping along from door to door, and the people usually took him in at public-houses where they knew him, and would give him drink and victuals, and sometimes farthings; and he in return would pipe and sing and talk simply, which diverted the people; and thus he lived. It was a very bad time for this diversion, yet the poor fellow went about as usual, but was almost starved; and when anybody asked how he did he would answer, the dead cart had not taken him yet, but that they had promised to call for him next week.

It happened one night that this poor fellow, whether some body had given him too much drink or no — John Hayward said he had no drink in his house, but that they had given him a little more victuals that ordinary at a public-house in Coleman Street — and the poor fellow, having not usually had a bellyful for perhaps a good while, was laid all along upon the top of a bulk or stall, and fast asleep, at a door in the street near London Wall, towards Cripplegate, and that upon the same bulk or stall the people of some house, in the alley of which the house was a corner, hearing a bell, which they always rang before the cart came, had laid a body really dead of the plague just by him, thinking too, that this poor fellow had been a dead body, as the other was, laid there by some of the neighbours.

Accordingly, when John Hayward with his bell and the cart came along, finding two dead bodies lie upon the stall, they took them up with the instrument they used and threw them into the cart, and all this while the piper slept soundly.

From hence they passed along and took in other dead bodies, till, as honest John Hayward told me, they almost buried the piper alive in the cart; yet all this while he slept soundly. At length the cart came to the place where the bodies were to be thrown into the ground, which, as I do remember, was at Mount Mill; and as the cart usually stopped some time before they were ready to shoot out the melancholy load they had in it, as soon as the cart stopped the fellow awaked and struggled a little to get his head out from among the dead bodies, when, raising himself up in the cart, he called out, "Hey; where am I?" This frighted the fellow that attended about the work; but after some pause John Hayward, recovering himself, said, "Lord, bless us! There's somebody in the cart not quite dead!" So another called to him and said, "Who are you?" The fellow answered, "I am the poor piper. Where am I?" "Where are you?" says Hayward. "Why, you are in the dead-cart, and we are going to bury you." "But I ain't dead though, am I?" says the piper, which made them laugh a little, though, as John said, they were heartily frighted at first; so they helped the poor fellow down, and he went about his business.

from
SOHRAB AND RUSTUM
by Matthew Arnold   3½

The Persian champion Rustum is faced by a Tartar opponent who is, in fact, his own son Sohrab — but neither knows the other's identity.

He spoke; and Sohrab kindled at his taunts,
And he too drew his sword: at once they rush'd
Together, as two eagles on one prey
Come rushing down together from the clouds,

One from the east, one from the West: their shields
Dash'd with a clang together, and a din
Rose, such as that the sinewy woodcutters
Make often in the forest's heart at morn,
Of hewing axes, crashing trees: such blows
Rustum and Sohrab on each other hail'd.
And you would say that sun and stars took part
In that unnatural conflict; for a cloud
Grew suddenly in Heaven, and dark'd the sun
Over the fighters' heads; and a wind rose
Under their feet, and moaning swept the plain,
And in a sandy whirlwind wrapp'd the pair.
In gloom they twain were wrapp'd, and they alone;
For both the on-looking hosts on either hand
Stood in broad daylight, and the sky was pure,
And the sun sparkled on the Oxus stream.
But in the gloom they fought, with bloodshot eyes
And labouring breath; first Rustum struck the shield
Which Sohrab held stiff out: the stell-spik'd spear
Rent the tough plates, but fail'd to reach the skin,
And Rustum pluck'd it back with angry groan.
Then Sohrab with his sword smote Rustum's helm,
Nor clove its steel quite through; but all the crest
He shore away, and that proud horsehair plume,
Never till now defil'd sunk to the dust;
And Rustum, bow'd his head; but then the gloom
Grew blacker: thunder rumbled in the air,
And lightnings rent the cloud; and Ruksh, the horse,
Who stood at hand, utter'd a dreadful cry:
No horse's cry was that, most like the roar
Of some pain'd desert lion, who all day
Has trail'd the hunter's javelin in his side,
And comes at night to die upon the sand:–
The two hosts heard that cry, and quak'd for fear,
And Oxus curdled as it cross'd his stream.
But Sohrab heard, and quail'd not, but rush'd on,
And struck again; and again Rustum bow'd
His head; but this time all the blade, like glass,

Sprang in a thousand shivers on the helm,
And in his hand the hilt remain'd alone.
Then Rustum rais'd his head: his dreadful eyes
Glar'd, and he shook on high his menacing spear,
And shouted, Rustum! *Sohrab heard that shout.*
And shrank amaz'd: back he recoil'd one step
And scann'd with blinking eyes the advancing Form:
And then he stood bewilder'd; and he dropp'd
His covering shield, and the spear pierc'd his side,
He reel'd, and staggering back, sunk to the ground.
And then the gloom dispers'd, and the wind fell,
The bright sun broke forth, and melted all
The cloud; and the two armies saw the pair;
Saw Rustum standing standing, safe upon his feet,
And Sohrab, wounded, on the bloody sand.

FRANKIE AND JOHNNY

Traditional   3½

[probably longer if you sing it!]

Frankie and Johnny were lovers,
Lordy, how they could love,
Swore to be true to each other,
True as the stars above,
    He was her man, but he done her wrong.

Little Frankie was a good gal,
As everybody knows,
She did all the work around the house,
And pressed her Johnny's clothes,
    He was her man, but he done her wrong.

Johnny was a yeller man,
With coal black, curly hair;
Everyone up in St Louis
Though he was a millionaire,
   He was her man, but he done her wrong.

Frankie went down to the bar-room,
Called for a bottle of beer,
Says, "Lookee here, Mister Bartender,
Has my lovin' Johnny been here?
   He is my man, and he's doin' me wrong."

"I will not tell you no story,
I will not tell you no lie.
Johnny left here about an hour ago,
With a gal named Nelly Bly,
   He is your man and he's doing you wrong."

Little Frankie went down Broadway,
With her pistol in her hand,
Said, "Stand aside you chorus gals,
I'm lookin' for my man,
   He is my man, and he's doin' me wrong."

The first time she shot him, he staggered,
The next time she shot him, he fell,
The last time she shot, O Lordy,
There was a new man's face in hell,
   She shot her man, for doin' her wrong.

"Turn me over doctor,
Turn me over slow,
I got a bullet in my left hand side,
Great God, it's hurtin' me so.
   I was her man, but I done her wrong."

It was a rubber-tyred buggy,
A decorated hack,
Took poor Johnny to the graveyard,
Brought little Frankie back,
    He was her man, but he done her wrong.

It was not murder in the first degree,
It was not murder in the third,
A woman simply dropped her man
Like a hunter drops his bird,
    She shot her man, for doin' her wrong.

The last time I saw Frankie,
She was sittin' in the 'lectric chair,
Waitin' to go and meet her God
V.'... ...e sweat runnin' out of her hair,
    She shot her man, for doin' her wrong.

Walked on down Broadway,
As far as I could see,
All I could hear was a two string bow
Playin' "Nearer my God to thee",
    He was her man, and he done her wrong.

● *It much disadvantageth the panegyrick of Synesius, and is no small*
disparagement unto baldness, if it be true what is related concerning
Aeschylus, whose bald pate was mistaken for a rock, and so was
brained by a tortoise which an eagle let fall upon it. Certainly it was
a very great mistake in the perspicacity of that animal.

(Sir Thomas Browne)

from
REYNARD THE FOX

by John Masefield 5½

The pure clean air came sweet to his lungs,
Till he thought foul scorn of those crying tongues.
In a three mile more he would reach the haven
In the Wan Dyke croaked on by the raven.
In a three mile more he would make his berth
On the hard cool floor of a Wan Dyke earth,
Too deep for spade, too curved for terrier,
With the pride of the race to make rest the merrier.
In a three mile more he would reach his dream,
So his game heart gulped and he put on steam.

Like a rocket shot to a ship ashore
The lean red bolt of his body tore,
Like a ripple of wind running swift on grass;
Like a shadow on wheat when a cloud blows past,
Like a turn at the buoy in a cutter sailing
When the bright green gleam lips white at the railing,
Like the April snake whipping back to sheath,
Like the gannets' hurtle on fish beneath,
Like a kestrel chasing, like a sickle reaping,
Like all things swooping, like all things sweeping,
Like a hound for stay, like a stag for swift,
With his shadow beside like spinning drift.

Past the gibbet-stock all stuck with nails,
Where they hanged in chains what had hung in jails,
Past Ashmundshowe where Ashmund sleeps,
And none but the tumbling peewit weeps,
Past Curlew Calling, the gaunt grey corner

Where the curlew comes as a summer mourner,
Past Blowbury Beacon, shaking his fleece,
Where all winds hurry and none brings peace;
Then down on the mile-long green decline,
Where the turf's like spring and the air's like wine,
Where the sweeping spurs of the downland spill,
Into Wan Brook Valley and Wan Dyke Hill.

On he went with a galloping rally
Past Maesbury Clump for Wan Brook Valley.
The blood in his veins went romping high,
"Get on, on, on, to the earth or die."
The air of the downs went purely past
Till he felt the glory of going fast,
Till the terror of death, though there indeed,
Was lulled for a while by his pride of speed.
He was romping away from hounds and hunt,
He had Wan Dyke Hill and his earth in front,
In a one mile more when his point was made
He would rest in safety from dog or spade;
Nose between paws he would hear the shout
Of the "Gone to earth!" to the hounds without,
The whine of the hounds, and their cat-feet gadding,
Scratching the earth, and their breath pad-padding:
He would hear the horn call hounds away,
And rest in peace till another day.

In one mile he would lie at rest,
So for one mile more he would go his best.
He reached the dip at the long droop's end,
And he took what speed he had still to spend.

As he raced the corn towards Wan Dyke Brook
The pack had view of the way he took;
Robin hallooed from the downland's crest,
He capped them on till they did their best.
The quarter-mile to the Wan Brook's brink
Was raced as quick as a man can think.

And here, as he ran to the huntsman's yelling,
The fox first felt that the pace was telling;
His body and lungs seemed all grown old.
His legs less certain, his heart less bold,
The hound-noise nearer, the hill slope steeper,
The thud in the blood of his body deeper.
His pride in his speed, his joy in the race,
Were withered away, for what use was pace?
He had run his best, and the hounds ran better,
Then the going worsened, the earth was wetter.
Then his brush drooped down till it sometimes dragged,
And his fur felt sick and his chest was tagged
With taggles of mud, and his pads seemed lead,
It was well for him he'd an earth ahead.

Down he went to the brook and over,
Out of the corn and into the clover,
Over the slope that the Wan Brook drains,
Past Battle Tump where they earthed the Danes,
Then up the hill that the Wan Dyke rings
Where the Sarsen Stones stand grand like kings.

Seven Sarsens of granite grim,
As he ran them by they looked at him;
As he leaped the lip of their earthen paling
The hounds were gaining and he was failing.

He passed the Sarsens, he left the spur,
He pressed uphill to the blasted fir,
He slipped as he leaped the hedge; he slithered.
"He's mine," thought Robin. "He's done; he's dithered."

At the second attempt he cleared the fence,
He turned half-right where the gorse was dense,
He was leading the hounds by a furlong clear.
He was past his best, but his earth was near.
He ran up gorse to the spring of the ramp,
The steep green wall of the dead men's camp,

He sidled up it and scampered down
To the deep green ditch of the Dead Men's Town.

Within, as he reached that soft green turf,
The wind, blowing lonely, moaned like surf,
Desolate ramparts rose up steep
On either side, for the ghosts to keep.
He raced the trench, past the rabbit warren,
Close-grown with moss which the wind made barren;
He passed the spring where the rushes spread,
And there in the stones was his earth ahead.
One last short burst upon failing feet—
There life lay waiting, so sweet, so sweet,
Rest in a darkness, balm for aches.

The earth was stopped. It was barred with stakes.

AGAINST ISRAEL HANDS

from "Treasure Island"   8
by R.L. Stevenson

Jim Hawkins and the wounded coxswain, Israel Hands, are trying to sail the
Hispaniola *ashore by themselves — but they are enemies to each other.*

"Now," said Hands, "Look there; there's a pet bit for to beach a ship in. Fine
flat sand, never a catspaw [=*snag*], trees all round of it, and flowers a-blowing
like a garding [=*garden*] on that old ship."

"And once beached," I inquired, "how shall we get her off again?"

"Why, so," he replied; "you take a line ashore there on the other side at
low water: take a turn about one o' them big pines; bring it back, take a turn
round the capstan, and lie-to for the tide. Come high water, all hands take a
pull upon the line, and off she comes as sweet as natur'. And now, boy, you
stand by. We're near the bit now, and she's too much way on her. Starboard a

little — so — steady — starboard — larboard a little — steady — steady!"

So he issued his commands, which I breathlessly obeyed; till, all of a sudden, he cried, "Now, hearty, luff!" And I put the helm hard up, and the *Hispaniola* swung round rapidly, and ran stem on for the low wooded shore.

The excitement of these last manoeuvres had somewhat interfered with the watch I had kept hitherto, sharply enough, upon the coxswain. Even then I was still so much interested, waiting for the ship to touch, that I had quite forgot the peril that hung over my head, and stood craning over the starboard bulwarks and watching the ripples spreading wide before the bows. I might have fallen without a struggle for my life, had not a sudden disquietude seized upon me, and made me turn my head. Perhaps I had heard a creak, or seen his shadow moving with the tail of my eye; perhaps it was an instinct like a cat's; but, sure enough, when I looked round, there was Hands, already half-way towards me, with the dirk in his right hand.

We must both have cried out aloud when our eyes met; but while mine was the shrill cry of terror, his was a roar of fury like a charging bull's. At the same instant he threw himself, and I leapt sideways towards the bows. As I did so, I left hold of the tiller, which sprang sharp to leeward; and I think this saved my life, for it struck Hands across the chest, and stopped him, for the moment, dead.

Before he could recover, I was safe out of the corner where he had me trapped, with all the deck to dodge about. Just forward of the mainmast I stopped, drew a pistol from my pocket, took a cool aim, though he had already turned and was once more coming directly after me, and drew the trigger. The hammer fell, but there followed neither flash nor sound; the prming was useless with sea water. I cursed myself for my neglect. Why had not I, long before, reprimed and reloaded my only weapons? Then I should not have been, as now, a mere fleeing sheep before this butcher.

Wounded as he was, it was wonderful how fast he could move, his grizzled hair tumbling over his face, and his face itself as red as a red ensign with his haste and fury. I had no time to try my other pistol, nor, indeed, much inclination, for I was sure it would be useless. One thing I saw plainly: I must not simply retreat before him, or he would speedily hold me boxed me in the stern. Once so caught, and nine or ten inches of the blood-stained dirk would be my last experience on this side of eternity. I placed my palms against the mainmast, which was of a goodish bigness, and waited, every nerve upon the stretch.

Seeing that I meant to dodge, he also paused; and a moment or two passed

E

in feints on his part, and corresponding movements upon mine. It was such a game as I had often played at home about the rocks of Black Hill Cove; but never before, you may be sure, with such a wildly beating heart as now. Still, as I say, it was a boy's game, and I thought I could hold my own at it, against an elderly seaman with a wounded thigh. Indeed, my courage had begun to rise so high, that I allowed myself a few darting thoughts on what would be the end of the affair; and while I saw certainly that I could spin it out for long, I saw no hope of any ultimate escape.

Well, while things stood thus, suddenly the *Hispaniola* struck, staggered, ground for an instant in the sand, and then, swift as a blow, canted over to the port side, till the deck stood at an angle of forty-five degrees, and about a puncheon of water splashed into the scupper holes, and lay, in a pool, between the deck and bulwark.

We were both of us capsized in a second, and both of us rolled, almost together, into the scuppers; the dead Red-cap, with his arms still spread out, tumbling stiffly after us. So near were we, indeed, that my head came against the coxswain's foot with a crack that made my teeth rattle. Blow and all, I was the first afoot again; for Hands had got involved with the dead body. The sudden canting of the ship had made the deck no place for running on; I had to find some new way of escape, and that upon the instant, for my foe was almost touching me. Quick as thought I sprang into the mizzen shrouds, rattled up and over hand, and did not draw a breath till I was seated on the cross-trees.

I had been saved by being prompt; the dirk had struck not half a foot below me, as I pursued my upward flight; and there stood Israel Hands with his mouth open and his face upturned to mine, a perfect statue of surprise and disappointment.

Now that I had a moment to myself, I lost no time in changing the priming of my pistol, and then, having one ready for service, and to make assurance double sure, I proceeded to draw the load of the other, and recharge it afresh from the beginning.

My new employment struck Hands all of a heap; he began to see the dice going against him; and after an obvious hesitation, he also hauled himself heavily into the shrouds, and, with the dirk in his teeth, began slowly and painfully to mount. It cost him no end of time and groans to haul his wounded leg behind him; and I had quietly finished my arrangements before he was much more than a third of the way up. Then, with a pistol in either hand, I addressed him.

"One more step, Mr Hands," said I, "and I'll blow your brains out! Dead men don't bite, you know," I added, with a chuckle.

He stopped instantly. I could see by the working of his face that he was trying to think, and the process was so slow and laborious that in my new-found security, I laughed aloud. At last, with a swallow or two, he spoke, his face still wearing the same expression of extreme perplexity. In order to speak he had to take the dagger from his mouth, but in all else he remained unmoved.

"Jim," says he, "I reckon we're fouled, you and me, and we'll have to sign articles [= *make peace*]. I'd have had you but for that there lurch; but I don't have no luck, not I; and I reckon I'll have to strike [= *give in*], which comes hard, you see, for a master mariner, to a ship's younker like you, Jim."

I was drinking in his words and smiling away, as conceited as a cock upon a wall, when, all in a breath, back went his right hand over his shoulder. Something sang like an arrow through the air; I felt a blow and then a sharp pang, and there I was pinned by the shoulder to the mast. In the horrid pain and surprise of the moment − I scarce can say it was by my own volition [= *intention*], and I am sure it was without a conscious aim − both my pistols went off, and both escaped out of my hands. They did not fall alone; with a choked cry, the coxswain loosed his grasp upon the shouds, and plunged head first into the water.

THE REVENGE

(A Ballad of the Fleet)   9
by Alfred, Lord Tennyson

At Florés in the Azores Sir Richard Grenville lay,
And a pinnace, like a fluttered bird, came flying from far away:
"Spanish ships of war at sea! we have sighted fifty-three!"
Then sware Lord Thomas Howard: " 'Fore God I am no coward;
But I cannot meet them here, for my ships are out of gear,
And half my men are sick. I must fly, but follow quick.
We are six ships of the line; can we fight with fifty-three?"

Then spake Sir Richard Grenville: "I know you are no coward;
You fly them for a moment to fight with them again.
But I've ninety men and more that are lying sick ashore.
I should count myself the coward if I left them, my Lord Howard,
To these Inquisition dogs and the devildoms of Spain."

So Lord Howard passed away with five ships of war that day,
Till he melted like a cloud in the silent summer heaven;
But Sir Richard bore in hand all his sick men from the land
Very carefully and slow,
Men of Bideford in Devon,
And we laid them on the ballast down below;
For we brought them all aboard,
And they blessed him in their pain, that they were not left to Spain,
To the thumbscrew and the stake, for the glory of the Lord.

He had only a hundred seamen to work the ship and to fight,
And he sailed away from Florés till the Spaniard came in sight,
With his huge sea-castles heaving upon the weather bow.
"Shall we fight or shall we fly?
Good Sir Richard, tell us now,
For to fight is but to die!
There'll be little of us left by the time this sun be set."
And Sir Richard said again: "We be all good English men.
Let us bang those dogs of Seville, the children of the devil,
For I never turned my back upon Don or devil yet."

Sir Richard spoke and he laughed, and we roared a hurrah, and so
The little Revenge ran on sheer into the heart of the foe,
With her hundred fighters on deck, and her ninety sick below;
For half their fleet to the right and half to the left were seen,
And the little Revenge ran on through the long sea-lane between.

Thousands of soldiers looked down from their decks and laughed.
Thousands of their seamen made mock at the mad little craft
Running on and on, till delayed
By their mountain-like San Philip that, of fifteen hundred tons,
And up-shadowing high above us with her yawning tiers of guns,
Took the breath from our sails, and we stayed.

And while now the great San Philip hung above us like a cloud
Whence the thunderbolt will fall
Long and loud,
Four galleons drew away
From the Spanish Fleet that day,
And two upon the larboard and two upon the starboard lay,
And the battle thunder broke from them all.

But anon the great San Philip, she bethought herself and went,
Having that within her womb that had left her ill content;
And the rest they came aboard us, and they fought us hand to hand,
For a dozen times they came with their pikes and musqueteers,
And a dozen times we shook 'em off as a dog that shakes his ears
When he leaps from the water to the land.

And the sun went down, and the stars came out far over the summer sea,
But never a moment ceased the fight of the one and the fifty-three.
Ship after ship, the whole night long, their high-built galleons came,
Ship after ship, the whole night long, with her battle-thunder and flame;
Ship after ship, the whole night long, drew back with her dead and her shame.
For some were sunk and many were shattered, and so could fight us no more—
God of battles, was ever a battle like this in the world before?

For he said, "Fight on! fight on!"
Though his vessel was all but a wreck;
And it chanced that, when half of the short summer night was gone,
With a grisly wound to be dressed he had left the deck,
But a bullet struck him that was dressing it suddenly dead,
And himself he was wounded again in the side and the head,
And he said, "Fight on! fight on!"

And the night went down and the sun smiled out far over the summer sea,
And the Spanish fleet with broken sides lay round us all in a ring;
But they dared not touch us again, for they feared that we still could sting,
So they watched what the end would be.
And we had not fought them in vain,
But in perilous plight were we,
Seeing forty of our poor hundred were slain,

And half of the rest of us maimed for life
In the crash of the cannonades and the desperate strife;
And the sick men down in the hold were most of them stark and cold,
And the pikes were all broken or bent, and the powder was all of it spent;
And the masts and the rigging were lying over the side;
But Sir Richard cried in his English pride,
"We have fought such a fight for a day and a night
As may never be fought again!
We have won great glory, my men!
And a day less or more
At sea or ashore,
We die—does it matter when?
Sink me the ship, Master Gunner—sink her, split her in twain!
Fall into the hands of God, not into the hands of Spain!"

And the gunner said, "Ay, ay," but the seamen made reply:
"We have children, we have wives,
And the Lord hath spared our lives.
We will make the Spaniard promise, if we yield, to let us go;
We shall live to fight again and to strike another blow."
And the lion there lay dying, and they yielded to the foe.

And the stately Spanish men to their flagship bore him then,
Where they laid him by the mast, old Sir Richard caught at last,
And they praised him to his face with their courtly foreign grace;
But he rose upon their decks, and he cried:
"I have fought for Queen and Faith like a valiant man and true;
I have only done my duty as a man is bound to do;
With a joyful spirit I Sir Richard Grenville die!"
And he fell upon their decks, and he died.

And they stared at the dead that had been so valiant and true,
And had holden the power and glory of Spain so cheap
That he dared her with one little ship and his English few;
Was he devil or man? He was devil for aught they knew,
But they sank his body with honour down into the deep,
And they manned the Revenge with a swarthier alien crew,
And away she sailed with her loss and longed for her own;

When a wind from the lands they had ruined awoke from sleep,
And the water began to heave and the weather to moan,
And or ever that evening ended a great gale blew,
And a wave like the wave that is raised by an earthquake grew,
Till it smote on their hulls and their sails and their masts and their flags,
And the whole sea plunged and fell on the shot-shattered navy of Spain,
And the little Revenge herself went down by the island crags
To be lost evermore in the main.

THOUSAND POUND PULL

from "The Call of the Wild"   11½
by Jack London

The dog Buck has recently saved his master, John Thornton, from drowning in Alaskan waters.

That winter, at Dawson, Buck performed another exploit, not so heroic, perhaps, but one that put his name many notches higher on the totem-pole of Alaskan fame. It was brought about by a conversation in the Eldorado Saloon, in which men waxed boastful of their favourite dogs. Buck, because of his record, was the target for these men, and Thornton was driven stoutly to defend him. At the end of half an hour one man stated that his dog could start a sled with five hundred pounds and walk off with it; a second bragged six hundred for his dog; and a third, seven hundred.

"Pooh! Pooh!" said John Thornton; "Buck can start a thousand pounds."

"And break it out? And walk off with it for a hundred yards?" demanded Matthewson, a Bonanza King, he of the seven hundred vaunt.

"And break it out, and walk off with it for a hundred yards," John Thornton said coolly.

"Well," Matthewson said, slowly and deliberately, so that all could hear, "I've got a thousand dollars that says he can't. And there it is." So saying, he slammed a sack of gold dust of the size of a bologna sausage down upon the bar.

Nobody spoke. Thornton's bluff, if bluff it was, had been called. He could feel a flush of warm blood creeping up his face. His tongue had tricked him. He did not know whether Buck could start a thousand pounds. Half a ton! The enormousness of it appalled him. He had great faith in Buck's strength and had often thought him capable of starting such a load; but never, as now, had he faced the possibility of it, the eyes of a dozen men fixed upon him, silent and waiting. Further, he had no thousand dollars; nor had Hans or Pete.

"I've got a sled standing outside now, with twenty fifty-pound sacks of flour on it," Matthewwson went on with brutal directness; "so don't let that hinder you."

Thornton did not reply. He did not know what to say. He glanced from face to face in the absent way of a man who has lost the power of thought and is seeking somewhere to find the thing that will start it going again. The face of Jim O'Brien, a Mastodon King and old-time comrade, caught his eyes. It was as a cue to him, seeming to rouse him to do what he would never have dreamed of doing.

"Can you lend me a thousand?" he asked, almost in a whisper.

"Sure," answered O'Brien, thumping down a plethoric [= *bulging*] sack by the side of Matthewson's. "Though it's little faith I'm having, John, that the beast can do the trick."

The Eldorado emptied its occupants into the street to see the test. The tables were deserted, and the dealers and game-keepers came forth to see the outcome of the wager and to lay odds. Several hundred men, furred and mittened, banked around the sled within easy distance. Matthewson's sled, loaded with a thousand pounds of flour, had been standing for a couple of hours, and in the intense cold (it was sixty below zero) the runners had frozen fast to the hard-packed snow. Men offered odds of two to one that Buck could not budge the sled. A quibble arose concerning the phrase "break out". O'Brien contended that it was Thornton's privilege to knock the runners loose, leaving Buck to "break it out" from a dead standstill. Matthewson insisted that the phrase included breaking the runners from the frozen grip of the snow. A majority of men who had witnessed the making of the bet decided in his favour, whereat the odds went up to three to one against Buck.

There were no takers. Not a man believed him capable of the feat. Thornton had been hurried into the wager, heavy with doubt; and now that he looked at the sled itself, the concrete fact, with the regular team of ten dogs curled up in the snow before it, the more impossible the task appeared. Matthewson waxed jubilant.

"Three to one!" he proclaimed. "I'll lay you another thousand at that figure, Thornton. What d'ye say?"

Thornton's doubt was strong in his face, but his fighting spirit was aroused — the fighting spirit that soars above odds, fails to recognize the impossible, and is deaf to all save the clamour for battle. He called Hans and Pete to him. Their sacks were slim, and with his own the three partners could rake together only two hundred dollars. In the ebb of their fortunes, this sum was their total capital; yet they laid it unhesitatingly against Matthewson's six hundred.

The team of ten dogs was unhitched, and Buck, with his own harness, was put in the sled. He had caught the contagion of the excitement, and he felt that in some way he must do a great thing for John Thornton. Murmurs of admiration at his splendid appearance went up. He was in perfect condition, without an ounce of superfluous flesh, and the one hundred and fifty pounds that he weighed were so many pounds of grit and virility. His furry coat shone with the sheen of silk. Down the neck and across the shoulders, his mane, in repose as it was, half bristled and seemed to lift with every movement, as though excess of vigour made each particular hair alive and active. The great breast and heavy forelegs were no more than in proportion with the rest of the body, where the muscles showed in tight rolls underneath the skin. Men felt these muscles and proclaimed them hard as iron, and the odds went down to two to one.

"Gad, sir! Gad, sir!" stuttered a member of the latest dynasty, a king of the Skookum Benches. "I offer you eight hundred for him, sir, before the test, sir; eight hundred just as he stands."

Thornton shook his head and stepped to Buck's side.

"You must stand off from him," said Matthewson protested. "Free play and plenty of room."

The crown fell silent; only could be heard the voices of the gamblers vainly offering two to one. Everybody acknowledged Buck a magnificent animal, but twenty fifty-pound sacks of flour bulked too large in their eyes for them to loosen their pouch-strings.

Thornton knelt down by Buck's side. He took his head in his two hands and rested cheek on cheek. He did not playfully shake him, as was his wont, or murmur soft love curses; but he whispered in his ear. "As you love me, Buck. As you love me," was what he whispered. Buck whined with suppressed eagerness.

The crowd was watching curiously . The affair was growing mysterious. It seemed like a conjuration. As Thornton got to his feet, Buck seized his mittened hand between his jaws, pressing in with his teeth and releasing slowly, half-reluctantly. It was the answer, in terms, not of speech, but of love; Thornton stepped well back.

"Now, Buck," he said.

Buck tightened the traces, than slacked them for a matter of several inches. It was the way he had learned.

"Gee!" Thornton's voice rang out, sharp in the tense silence.

Buck swung to the right ending the movement in a plunge that took up the slack and with a sudden jerk arrested his one hundred and fifty pounds. The load quivered, and from under the runners arose a crisp crackling.

"Haw!" Thornton commanded.

Buck duplicated the manoeuvre, this time to the left. The crackling turned into a snapping, the sled pivoting and the runners slipping and grating several inches to the side. The sled was broken out. Men were holding their breaths, intensely unconscious of the fact.

"Now, MUSH!"

Thornton's command cracked out like a pistol-shot. Buck threw himself forward, tightening the traces with a jarring lunge. His whole body was gathered compactly together in the tremendous effort, the muscles writhing and knotting like live things under the silky fur. His great chest was low to the ground, his head forward and down, while his feet were flying like mad, the claws scarring the hard-packed snow in parallel grooves. The sled swayed and trembled, half-started forward. One of his feet slipped, and one man groaned aloud. Then the sled lurched ahead in what appeared a rapid succession of jerks, though it never really came to a dead stop again . . . half an inch . . . two inches . . . . The jerks perceptibly diminished; as the sled gained momentum, he caught them up, till it was moving steadily along.

Men gasped and began to breathe again, unaware that for a moment, they had ceased to breathe. Thornton was running behind, encouraging Buck with short, cheery words. The distance had been measured off, and as he neared the pile of firewood which marked the end of the hundred yards, a cheer began to grow and grow, which burst into a roar as he passed the firewood and halted at command. Every man was tearing himself loose, even Matthewson. Hats and mittens were flying in the air. Men were shaking hands, it did not matter with whom, and bubbling over in a general incoherent babel.

But Thornton fell on his knees beside Buck. Head was against head, and he was shaking him back and forth. Those who hurried up heard him cursing

Buck, and he cursed him long and fervently, and softly and lovingly.

"Gad, sir! Gad, sir!" spluttered the Skookum Bench king. "I'll give you a thousand for him, sir, a thousand, sir — twelve hundred, sir!"

Thornton rose to his feet. His eyes were wet. The tears were streaming frankly down his cheeks. "Sir," he said to the Skookum Bench king, "no, sir. You can go to hell, sir. It's the best I can do for you, sir."

SREDNI VASHTAR
by "Saki"   12½
                                                                            [11]

Conradin was ten years old, and the doctor had pronounced his professional opinion that the boy would not live another five years. The doctor was silky and effete, and counted for little, but his opinion was endorsed by Mrs De Ropp, who counted for nearly everything. Mrs De Ropp was Conradin's cousin and guardian, and in his eyes she represented those three-fifths of the world that are necessary and disagreeable and real; the other two-fifths, in perpetual antagonism to the foregoing, were summed up in himself and his imagination. [One of these days Conradin supposed he would succumb to the mastering pressure of wearisome necessary things — such as illnesses and coddling restrictions and drawn-out dullness. Without his imagination, which was rampant under the spur of loneliness, he would have succumbed long ago.]

Mrs De Ropp would never, in her honestest moments, have confessed to herself that she disliked Conradin, though she might have been dimly aware that thwarting him "for his good" was a duty which she did not find particularly irksome. Conradin hated her with a desperate sincerity which he was perfectly able to mask. [Such few pleasures as he could contrive for himself gained an added relish from the likelihood that they would be displeasing to his guardian, and from the realm of his imagination she was locked out — an unclean thing, which should find no entrance.]

In the dull, cheerless garden, overlooked by so many windows that were ready to open with a message not to do this or that, or a reminder that medicines were due, he found little attraction. [The few fruit-trees that it contained were set jealously apart from his plucking, as though they were rare specimens of their kind blooming in an arid waste; it would probably have been difficult to find a market-gardener who would have offered ten shillings for their entire yearly produce.] In a forgotten corner, however, almost hidden behind a dismal shrubbery, was a disused tool-shed of respectable proportions, and within its walls Conradin found a haven, something that took on the varying aspects of a playroom and a cathedral. He had peopled it with a legion of familiar phantoms, evoked partly from fragments of history and partly from his own brain, but it also boasted two inmates of flesh and blood. In one corner lived a ragged-plumaged Houdan hen, on which the boy lavished an affection that had scarcely another outlet. Further back in the gloom stood a large hutch, divided into two compartments, one of which was fronted with close iron bars. This was the abode of a large polecat-ferret, which a friendly butcher-boy had once smuggled, cage and all, into its present quarters, in exchange for a long-secreted hoard of small silver. Conradin was dreadfully afraid of the lithe, sharp-fanged beast, but it was his most treasured possession. Its very presence in the tool-shed was a secret and fearful joy, to be kept scrupulously from the knowledge of the Woman, as he privately dubbed his cousin. And one day, out of Heaven knows what material, he spun the beast a wonderful name, and from that moment it grew into a god and a religion. [The Woman indulged in religion once a week at a church near by, and took Conradin with her, but to him the church service was an alien rite in the House of Rimmon.] Every Thursday, in the dim and musty silence of the tool-shed, he worshipped with mystic and elaborate ceremonial before the wooden hutch where dwelt Sredni Vashtar, the great ferret. Red flowers in their season and scarlet berries in the winter-time were offered at his shrine, for he was a god who laid some special stress on the fierce impatient side of things, as opposed to the Woman's religion, which, as far as Conradin could observe, went to great lengths in the contrary direction. And on great festivals powdered nutmeg was strewn in front of his hutch, an important feature of the offering being that the nutmeg had to be stolen. These festivals were of irregular occurrence, and were chiefly appointed to celebrate some passing event. On one occasion, when Mrs De Ropp suffered from acute toothache for three days. Conradin kept up the festival during the entire three days, and almost succeeded in persuading himself that Sredni Vashtar was personally responsible for the toothache. If the malady had lasted for another day the supply of nutmeg would have given out.

[The Houdan hen was never drawn into the cult of Sredni Vashtar. Conradin had long ago settled that she was an Anabaptist. He did not pretend to have the remotest knowledge as to what an Anabaptist was, but he privately hoped that it was dashing not very respectable. Mrs De Ropp was the ground plan on which he based and detested all respectability.]

After a while Conradin's absorption in the tool-shed began to attract the notice of his guardian. "It is not good for him to be pottering down there in all weathers," she promptly decided, and at breakfast one morning she announced that the Houdan hen had been sold and taken away overnight. With her short-sighted eyes she peered at Conradin, waiting for an outbreak of rage and sorrow, which she was ready to rebuke with a flow of excellent precepts and reasoning. But Conradin said nothing: there was nothing to be said. Something perhaps in his white set face gave her a momentary qualm, for at tea that afternoon there was toast on the table, a delicacy which she usually banned on the ground that it was bad for him; also because the making of it "gave trouble," a deadly offence in the middle-class feminine eye.

"I thought you liked toast," she exclaimed, with an injured air, observing that he did not toucn it.

"Sometimes," said Conradin.

In the shed that evening there was innovation in the worship of the hutch-god. Conradin had been wont to chant his praises, tonight he asked a boon.

"Do one thing for me, Sredni Vashtar."

The thing was not specified. As Sredni Vashtar was a god he must be supposed to know. And choking back a sob as he looked at that other empty corner, Conradin went back to the world he so hated.

And every night, in the welcome darkness of his bedroom, and every evening in the dusk of the tool-shed, Conradin's bitter litany went up: "Do one thing for me, Sredni Vashtar."

Mrs De Ropp noticed that the visits to the shed did not cease, and one day she made a further journey of inspection.

"What are you keeping in that locked hutch?" she asked. "I believe it's guinea-pigs. I'll have them all cleared away."

Conradin shut his lips tight, but the Woman ransacked his bedroom till she found the carefully hidden key, and forthwith marched down to the shed to complete her discovery. It was a cold afternoon, and Conradin had been bidden to keep to the house. From the furthest window of the dining-room the door of the shed could just be seen beyond the corner of the shrubbery, and there Conradin stationed himself. He saw the Woman enter, and then he imagined her opening the door of the sacred hutch and peering down with her short-sighted eyes into the thick straw bed where his god lay hidden. Perhaps she would prod at the straw in her clumsy impatience. And Conradin fervently breathed his prayer for the last time. But he knew as he prayed that he did not believe. He knew that the Woman would come out presently with that pursed smile he loathed so well on her face, and that in an hour or two the gardener would carry away his wonderful god, a god no longer, but a simple brown ferret in a hutch. And he knew that the Woman would triumph always as she triumphed now, and that he would grow ever more sickly under her pestering and domineering and superior wisdom, till one day nothing would matter much more with him, and the doctor would be proved right. And in the sting and misery of his defeat, he began to chant loudly and defiantly the hymn of his threatened idol:

> *Sredni Vashtar went forth,*
> *His thoughts were red thoughts and his teeth were white.*
> *His enemies called for peace, but he brought them death.*
> *Sredni Vashtar the Beautiful.*

And then of a sudden he stopped his chanting and drew closer to the window-pane. The door of the shed still stood ajar as it had been left, and the minutes were slipping by. They were long minutes, but they slipped by nevertheless. He watched the starlings running and flying in little parties across the lawn; he counted them over and over again, with one eye always on that swinging door. A sour-faced maid came in to lay the table for tea, and still Conradin stood and waited and watched. Hope had crept by inches into his heart, and now a look of triumph began to blaze in his eyes that had only known the the wistful patience of defeat. Under his breath, with a furtive exultation, he began once again the paean of victory and devastation. And presently his eyes were rewarded; out through that doorway came a long, low, yellow-and-brown beast, with eyes a-blink at the waning daylight, and dark wet stains around the fur of jaws and throat. Conradin dropped on his knees. The great polecat-ferret made its way down to a small brook at the foot of the garden, drank for a moment, then crossed a little plank bridge and was lost to sight in the bushes. Such was the passing of Sredni Vashtar.

"Tea is ready," said the sour-faced maid; "where is the mistress?"

"She went down to the shed some time ago," said Conradin.

And while the maid went to summon her mistress to tea, Conradin fished a toasting-fork out of the sideboard drawer and proceeded to toast himself a piece of bread. And during the toasting of it and the buttering of it with much butter and the slow enjoyment of eating it, Conradin listened to the noises and silences which fell in quick spasms beyond the dining-room door. The loud foolish screaming of the maid, the answering chorus of wondering ejaculations from the kitchen region, the scuttering footsteps and hurried embassies for outside help, and then, after a lull, the scared sobbings and the shuffling tread of those who bore a heavy burden into the house.

"Whoever will break it to the poor child? I couldn't for the life of me!" exclaimed a shrill voice. And while they debated the matter among themselves, Conradin made himself another piece of toast.

THE TRUCE OF THE BEAR
by "Sapper" 14½
[12½]

A contrast of North America with the trench-world of the Ist World War – The Germans are referred to both as Huns and Boches.

> *When he stands up as pleading, in wavering man-brute guise,*
> *When he veils the hate and cunning of the little swinish eyes,*
> *When he shows as seeking quarter, with paws like hands in prayer,*
> *That is the time of peril – the time of the Truce of the Bear!*

I

Over the land lay the Great White Silence. Rugged and beetling, with the sentinel pines creaking eerily on its slopes, the ridge stretched away to the North – to the land where the lights of opal and gold quiver and tremble in the skies, till the glory of them makes the beholder cover his face. From below, the ceaseless roar of the torrent, rushing through the gloom of the canyon, came monotonously to the ear of the man who crouched motionless beside one of the bleak firs. His keen eyes, steady and sharp as those of a lynx, were fixed unblinkingly on an opening in the hillside twenty yards away. and in his hands, cradled in the grey moss round the tree-trunk, he held a rifle. The pines were singing the song of the ages, with the icy wind from the everlasting snows as the accompaniment; but to the man it was just the solitude that he loved, the voice of the wild, the hush of the lone North mountains. He seemed not to feel the cold; remorseless and still he crouched there watching, the only human being in the whole mighty wilderness.

Suddenly he stiffened, and his grip tightened on the rifle. So small was the movement as to be almost imperceptible, and to a townsman, even if he had seen it, its reason would not have been clear. Apparently everything was just the same. The roar of the waters, the sighing wind moaning through the tops of the trees, the brooding land bright in the icy moon – all was just the same. Nothing had altered to make the silent watcher catch his breath with a little short hiss, and his jaw set firm till it might have been chiselled in rock. Nothing, that is, to the onlooker. But then he would have been a townsman, and to such the Law of the Wild is a closed book. For the watcher had heard the sound he had been waiting for, and he knew that his vigil was nearly over.

Pig eyes glinting, head roving from side to side as he sniffed the air, there shambled from the hole a monstrous grizzly. For a few seconds he paused at the entrance to his cave, conscious that there was danger, but unable to see where it lay. Grunting, he looked round; then he shambled forward a few paces, and stopped again; while the man waited, so motionless, that he hardly seemed to breathe. Then the bear saw him and roared – a snarling roar of rage and fear. Man – the Lord of the Wild Things – had tracked him to his lair, and he knew what that meant. That silent, menacing figure, whose eyes seemed to bore into him, and whose hands held the stick of death – yes, he knew what that meant.

Suddenly he rose on his hind legs, and grunted again. If only he could get his enemy clasped once to him with those great hairy paws, if only he could squeeze and squeeze till the bones broke, if only – He shambled grotesquely forward swaying from side to side, revolting and horrible, like some hairy, prehistoric man. He groaned and chuckled, "with paws like hands in prayer," and then –

Through the mountain vastness an echo rang and was flung to the ravines on high. It mocked the sighing wind, it drowned the roar of the water, until, at length, it died away, lost and whispering in the everlasting snows.

With a grunt of satisfaction the man stepped out and shook himself.

"It's when you plead and pray that I don't like you, cully," he said softly, touching the quivering carcase with his boot. "It's the only time you're really dangerous."

II

Over the land lay the Great Grey Silence. A vast expanse of sticky slime stretched as far as the eye could see. Away to the left a charred skeleton house, surrounded by some splintered toothpick trees, stuck out of the stagnant ooze. Every now and then would come a great rushing noise, followed by the roar of an explosion, and from the face of a desolate world there would shoot up a sullen stifling cloud of black and yellow fumes. Gradually it would drift away, and once again a dull-grey sky would look down on a dull-grey world. The only splashes of colour lay in the pools of water — and they were sombre; God knows they were sombre. In each of the countless holes, which grew like a loathsome disease all over the grey country, there lay a pool, a stinking, filthy pool. Sometimes it was green, and covered with a white scum; sometimes it was grey and lifeless, just like the hole it lay in; sometimes it was red —

Things stuck out of the pools — bits of equipment, bandoliers, tins of bully beef. In some a mule, its legs stiff and pointing, would lie upon its back at a strange angle, its eyes glazed and lifeless. In some a man would lie sprawling, head downwards in the water, with white chalky hands which had scrabbled in the mud, and now were still. In some a knee would stick up above the loathsome, fetid water; in some things floated — things not good to look upon.

Crouching, shivering in the holes, were men — grey men. The mud of the sides of the holes was like the mud under London Bridge when the river is low and in that mud lived the men. [Not in all the holes — only a selected few along the lines which had been reached in the last advance. And even along that line the holes which were occupied were not continuous. Scattered here and there, isolated and cut off little groups of men crouched and lived. Sometimes one of the clouds of black and yellow smoke would shoot up from an occupied hole. Then other things would go up with it, and when everything had cleared away the hole would have changed. The sides would be yellow and black save in one place where they were red, and sticking out of the pool, on which already the red scum was forming, would be a fragment. But it would not affect the other hole-dwellers. Probably they would know nothing of what had happened, and, even if they did, their job was to continue sitting on the side above the water. In fact, their only amusement was to cut a recess in the wet mud, in order to prevent themselves slipping down into the water. Sometimes an enthusiast would try and link up his hole with the next gentleman's; sometimes an inventive genius would try and drain his abode of bliss by cutting a trench into another unoccupied hole. But this latter pastime is not altogether to be recommended unless the cutter is quite sure of being able to put into practice the well-known theory that water does not flow uphill. It is most annoying, having cut the drain, to find that it is the other hole which empties into yours.]

In one of these holes, crouching in a little recess he had dug, there knelt a man. His face, his hands, his clothes were coated thick with half-congealed mud; only his eyes, steady and sharp as a lynx, were fixed unblinkingly on a spot in the grey sea twenty odd yards away. There was no sign of movement, there was nothing to distinguish the spot he was watching from the rest of the filthy slush, and yet for half an hour his eyes had never left it. The stinking earth in front was pitted and shattered, and glistened with the rainbow colours of wet mud, but the watcher's eyes were fixed on a gaping crack between two glutinous lumps. Cradled in his hand was a rifle – a rifle of which the sights were hidden and coated with the all-pervading mud, but a rifle in which the barrel was clean and shining. It didn't look much, that gun; it would have meant imprisonment for life on a rifle inspection; but it could be fired through, which was more than could be said for most of those that find their way to the Grey Land of Filth.

[The man had been there since the advance at dawn. The lines of wading, struggling men had slowly advanced, now slipping out of sight into the stagnant pools, now pausing to pluck themselves from the glue. They had reached their objective – the group of holes lately occupied by the Huns – and they had killed the occupiers. In some cases the occupiers had killed them, which is the whole of war when shorn of its trappings and reduced to the language of those who perform. And, having reached their objective, they sat there, until in the fullness of time other wading, struggling men would sog down beside them in their shell holes, and they would be relieved.]

Occasionally the onlooker might see a steel helmet move for a moment, in the huge sea of dirt, as a man's head came above ground-level; occasionally, in the distance, far back from the front line, a small party of men might be seen floundering and heaving its way along. Then if the party was not too far away there come a short, sharp crack, the hum of a rifle bullet, the "who-e-e" as it passed into the distance, and the party would duck hurriedly and disappear. They were being sniped – sniped from one of the countless holes that go to make the disease called Flanders. And one of the British snipers was the man who crouched in the hole, watching.

Up to date he had had ten targets, and he believed that six had been bulls. When a man can really shoot with a rifle, there is a sort of sixth sense which tells him when he's scored – a sense which tells him the difference between the man who ducks because it was near and the man who ducks because he is dead. It had amused him vastly through the long weary hours lying there, watching, waiting, and – then, the kick of the gun in his shoulder as he got his quarry on the foresight, the slow lifting of his cheek from the stock to watch the result. Twice had he seen his target throw up his hands and pitch forward, and one of those he could still see – a motionless lump sprawling out of a shell hole. And for the others – well, he hoped for the best with four, as I have said.

But for the last half-hour he had not been firing. Two good targets had come and gone, and he had watched them regretfully out of the corner of his eye, but he had made no attempt to fire at them; he had continued lying motionless, watching the spot a score of yards away.

Suddenly he stiffened, and his grip tightened on the rifle. So small was the movement as to be almost imperceptible, and to the onlooker, even if he had seen it, its reason would not have been clear. Apparently everything was just the same. The grey stagnant sea, the charred skeleton houses surrounded by the splintered toothpick trees – it was all just the same. Nothing had altered, except that the silent watcher had seen what he was waiting for, and he knew that his vigil was nearly over.

Through the crack between the two glutinous lumps, there had shone for a moment a chink of light, and a little blob of mud had slipped forward. A hole made by a man's finger had appeared, and the sniper knew that he was being watched. Snipers are not popular with those they snipe.

And now he was waiting for the next move in the game of no mistakes.

It came quite quickly.

"Kamerad!" A voice hailed him – a voice with no visible owner. "Kamerad! I to surrender wish! Kamerad!"

"Then come over here with your hands up, Boche." The sniper's voice, quick and incisive, answered the unseen speaker. "And keep your hands up, Boche."

With his eyes unblinking, with his body so motionless that he hardly seemed to breathe, the sniper waited, his rifle still cuddled to his cheek. Suddenly a figure half rose, half shambled out of the ground in front. It was a grey-clad figure, and the face was coated grey, too. Only the eyes − pig eyes − roved from side to side, as he looked for the sniper, and his arms and hands were raised as though in prayer. And then−

Over the desolate flatness a vicious crack rang out, and, mingled with it, the sullen phlop of a bullet which finds its mark at close range. It did not echo; there was nothing to cause an echo. It was, one moment, the next it was not.

With a grunt of satisfaction the man lowered his rifle and shook himself.

"It's when you plead and pray that I don't like you, cully," he said softly, watching the quivering carcase in front. "It's the only time you're really dangerous."

You see it is the game of no mistakes, and the Boche had made one. He had failed to conceal the bomb in his hands − the hands that were raised in prayer.

ICE COLD

from "H.M.S. Ulysses"   15½
by Alistair Maclean.

Nicholls and Carpenter (nicknamed "the Kapok Kid" because of his special quilted suiting) are officers aboard the Ulysses. *Carrington is First Officer: Tyndall, Rear-Admiral.*

"What do you make of it, Captain? Prospects aren't altogether healthy, are they?"

"We're for it, sir. It's really piling up against us. Carrington has spent six years in the West Indies, has gone through a dozen hurricanes. Admits he's seen a barometer lower, but never one so low with the pressure still falling so fast − not in these latitudes. This is only a curtain-raiser."

"This will do me nicely, meantime, thank you," Tyndall said dryly. "For a curtain-raiser, it's doing not so badly."

It was a masterly understatement. For a curtain-raiser, it was a magnificent performance. The wind was fairly steady, about Force 9 on the Beaufort scale, and the snow had stopped. A temporary cessation only, they all knew — far ahead to the north-west the sky was a peculiarly livid colour. It was a dull glaring purple, neither increasing nor fading, faintly luminous and vaguely menacing in its uniformity and permanence. Even to men who had seen everything the Arctic skies had to offer, from pitchy darkness on a summer's noon, right through the magnificent displays of Northern Lights to that wonderfully washed-out blue that so often smiles down on the stupendous calms of the milk-white seas that lap edge of the Barrier, this was something quite unknown.

But the Admiral's reference had been to the sea. It had been building up, steadily, inexorably, all during the morning. Now, at noon, it looked uncommonly like an eighteenth century print of a barque in a storm — serried waves of greenish-grey, straight, regular and marching uniformly along, each decoratively topped with frothing caps of white. Only here, there were 500 feet between crest and crest, and the squadron, heading almost directly into it, was taking hearty punishment.

For the little ships, already burying their bows every fifteen seconds in a creaming smother of cascading white, this was bad enough, but another, a more dangerous and insidious enemy was at work — the cold. The temperature had long sunk below freezing point, and the mercury was still shrinking down, close towards the zero mark.

The cold was now intense: ice formed in cabins and mess-decks: fresh-water systems froze solid: metal contracted, hatch-covers jammed, door hinges locked in frozen immobility, the oil in the searchlight controls gummed up and made them useless. To keep a watch, especially a watch on the bridge, was torture: the first shock of that bitter wind seared the lungs, left a man fighting for breath: if he had forgotten to don gloves — first the silk gloves, then the woollen mittens, then the sheepskin gauntlets — and touched a handrail, the palms of the hands seared off, the skin burnt as by white-hot metal: on the bridge, if he forgot to duck when the bows smashed down into a trough, the flying spray, solidified in a second into hurtling slivers of ice, lanced cheek and forehead open to the bone: hands froze, the very marrow of the bones numbed, the deadly chill crept upwards from feet to calves to thighs, nose and chin turned white with frostbite and demanded immediate attention: and then, by far the worst of all. the end of the watch, the return below deck, the writhing, excruciating agony of returning circulation. But, for all this, words are useless things, pale shadows of reality. Some things lie beyond the knowledge and the experience of the majority of mankind, and here imagination finds itself in a world unknown.

But all these things were relatively trifles, personal inconveniences to be shrugged aside. The real danger lay elsewhere. It lay in the fact of ice.

There were over three hundred tons of it already on the decks of the *Ulysses*, and more forming every minute. It lay in a thick, even coat over the main deck, the fo'c'sle, the gun-decks and the bridges: it hung in long, jagged icicles from coamings and turrets and rails: it trebled the diameter of every wire, stay and halliard, and turned slender masts into monstrous trees, ungainly and improbable. It lay everywhere, a deadly menace, and much of the danger lay in the slippery surface it presented – a problem much more easily overcome on a coal-fired merchant ship with clinker and ashes from its boilers, than in the modern oil-fired warships. On the *Ulysses*, they spread salt and sand and hoped for the best.

But the real danger of the ice lay in its weight. A ship, to use technical terms, can be either stiff or tender. If she's stiff, she has a low centre of gravity, rolls easily, but whips back quickly and is extremely stable and safe. If she's tender, with a high centre of gravity, she rolls reluctantly but comes back even more reluctantly, is unstable and unsafe. And if a ship were tender, and hundreds of tons of ice piled high on its decks, the centre of gravity rose to a dangerous height. It could rise to a fatal height . . .

The escort carriers and the destroyers, especially the *Portpatrick*, were vulnerable, terribly so. The carriers, already unstable with the great height and weight of their reinforced flight-decks, provided a hugh, smooth, flat surface to the falling snow, ideal conditions for the formation of ice. Earlier on, it had been possible to keep the flight-decks relatively clear – working parties had toiled incessantly with brooms and sledges, salt and steam hoses. But the weather had deteriorated so badly now that to send out a man on that wildly pitching, staggering flight-deck, glassy and infinitely treacherous, would be to send him to his death. The *Wrestler* and *Blue Ranger* had modified heating systems under the flight-decks – modified, because, unlike the British ships, these Mississippi carriers had planked flight-decks: in such extreme conditions, they were hopelessly inefficient.

Conditions aboard the destroyers were even worse. They had to contend not only with the ice from the packed snow, but with ice from the sea itself. As regularly as clockwork, huge clouds of spray broke over the destroyer's fo'c'sles as the bows crashed solidly, shockingly into the trough and rising shoulder of the next wave: the spray froze as it touched the deck, even before it touched the deck, piling up the solid ice, in places over a foot thick, from the stem aft beyond the breakwater. The tremendous weight of the ice was pushing the little ships down by their heads; deeper, with each successive plunge ever deeper, they buried their noses in the sea, and each time, more and more sluggishly, more and more reluctantly, they staggered laboriously up from the depths. Like the carrier captains, the destroyer skippers could only look down from their bridges, helpless, hoping.

Two hours passed, two hours in which the temperature fell to zero, hesitated, then shrank steadily beyond it, two hours in which the barometer tumbled crazily after it. Curiously, strangely, the snow still held off, the livid sky to the north-west was as far away as ever, and the sky to the south and east had cleared completely. The squadron presented a fantastic picture now, little toy-boats of sugar-icing, dazzling white, gleaming and sparkling in the pale, winter sunshine, pitching crazily through the ever-lengthening, ever-deepening valleys of grey and green of the cold Norwegian Sea, pushing on towards that far horizon, far and weird and purply glowing, the horizon of another world. It was an incredibly lovely spectacle.

The wind was rising more quickly now and long ribbons of white were beginning to streak the water. Wave troughs were deepening rapidly, their sides steepening, their tops blown off and flattened by the wind. Gradually, but perceptibly to the ear now, the thin, lonely whining in the rigging was climbing steadily up the register. From time to time, large chunks of ice, shaken loose by the increasing vibration, broke off from the masts and stays and spattered on the deck below.

The effect of the long oil-slicks trailing behind the carriers was almost miraculous. The destroyers, curiously mottled with oil now, were still plunging astern, but the surface tension of the fuel held the water and spray from breaking aboard. Tyndall, justifiably, was feeling more than pleased with himself.

Towards half-past four in the afternoon, with shelter still a good fifteen miles away, the elation had completely worn off. There was a whole gale blowing now and Tyndall had been compelled to signal for a reduction in speed.

From deck level, the seas now were more than impressive. They were gigantic, frightening. Nicholls stood with the Kapok Kid, off watch now, on

the main deck, under the port whaler, sheltering in the lee of the fo'c'sle
deck. Nicholls, clinging to a davit to steady himself, and leaping back now and
then to avoid a deluge of spray, looked over to where the *Defender*, the
Vultra and *Viking* tailing behind, were pitching madly, grotesquely, under
that serene blue sky. The blue sky above, the tremendous seas below. There
was something almost evil, something literally spine-chilling, in that macabre
contrast.

The cold was vicious. The wind was tearing great gouts of water off the
wave-tops, driving the atomised spray at bullet speed against fo'c'sle and
sides. It was impossible to breathe without turning one's back, without
wrapping layers of wool round mouth and nose. Faces blue and white,
shaking violently with cold, neither suggested, neither even thought of going
below. Men hypnotised, men fascinated by the tremendous seas, the towering
waves, 1,000, 2,000 feet in length, long, sloping on the lee side, steep-walled
and terrifying on the other, pushed up by a sixty knot wind and by some
mighty force lying far to the north-west. In these gigantic troughs, a church
steeple would be lost for ever.

Both men turned round as they heart the screen door crashing behind
them. A duffel-coated figure, cursing fluently, fought to shut the heavy door
against the pitching of the *Ulysses*, finally succeeded in heaving the clips
home. It was Leading Seaman Doyle, and even though his beard hid
three-quarters of what could be seen of his face, he still looked thoroughly
disgusted with life.

Carpenter grinned him. He and Doyle had served a commission together on
the China Station. Doyle was a very privileged person.

"Well, well, the Ancient Mariner himself! How are things down below,
Doyle?"

"Bloody desperate, sir!" His voice was as lugubrious as his face. "Cold as
charity, sir, and everything all over the bloody place. Cups, saucers, plates in
smithereens. Half the crew —"

He broke off suddenly, eyes slowly widening in blank disbelief. He was
staring out to sea between Nicholls and Carpenter.

"Well, what about half the crew? . . . What's the matter, Doyle?"

"Christ Almighty!" Doyle's voice was slow, stunned: it was almost a
prayer. "Oh, Christ Almighty!" The voice rose sharply on the last two
syllables.

The two officers twisted round. The *Defender* was climbing — all 500 feet of her was literally climbing — up the lee side of a wave that staggered the imagination, whose immensity completely defied immediate comprehension. Even as they watched, before shocked minds could grasp the significance of it all, the *Defender* reached the crest, hesitated, crazily tilted up her stern till screw and rudder were entirely clear of the water, then crashed down, down, down . . .

Even at two cable-lengths' distance in that high wind, the explosive smash of the plummeting bows came like a thunder-clap. An aeon ticked by, and still the *Defender* seemed to keep on going under, completely buried now, right back to the bridge island, in a sea of foaming white. How long she remained like that, arrowed down into the depths of the Arctic, no one could afterwards say: then slowly, agonisingly, incredibly, great rivers of water cascaded off her bows, she broke surface again. Broke surface, to present to frankly disbelieving eyes a spectacle entirely without precedent, anywhere, at any time. The tremendous, instantaneous, up-thrusting pressure of unknown thousands of tons of water had torn the open flight-deck completely off its mountings and bent it backwards, in a great, sweeping "U," almost as far as the bridge. It was a sight to make men doubt their sanity, to leave them stupefied, to leave them speechless — all, that is, except the Kapok Kid. He rose magnificently to the occasion.

"My word!" he murmured thoughtfully. "That *is* unusual."

IN THE HOUSE OF SHAWS

from "Kidnapped"   16½
by R.L. Stevenson   [12½]

After the death of his father, David Balfour is staying with Uncle Ebenezer.

[For a day that was begun so ill, the day passed fairly well. We had the porridge cold again at noon, and hot porridge at night; porridge and small beer was my uncle's diet. He spoke but little, and that in the same way as before, shooting a question at me after a long silence; and when I sought to lead him in talk about my future, slipped out of it again. In a room next door to the kitchen, where he suffered me to go, I found a great number of books, both Latin and English, in which I took great pleasure all the afternoon. Indeed, the time passed so lightly in this good company that I began to almost reconciled to my residence at Shaws; and nothing but the sight of my uncle, eyes playing hide and seek with mine, revived the force of my distrust.

One thing I discovered which put me in some doubt. This was an entry on the fly-leaf of a chap-book (one of Patrick Walker's) plainly written by my father's hand and thus conceived: "To my brother Ebenezer on his fifth birthday." Now, what puzzled me was this; That, as my father was, of course, the younger brother, he must either have made some strange error, or he must have written, before he was yet five, an excellent, clear, manly hand of writing.

I tried to get this out of my head; but though I took down many interesting authors, old and new, history, poetry, and story-book, this notion of my father's hand of writing stuck to me; and when at length I went back into the kitchen, and sat down once more to porridge and small beer, the first thing I said to Uncle Ebenezer was to ask him if my father had not been very quick at his book.

"Alexander? No him!" was the reply. "I was far quicker mysel'; I was a clever chappie when I was young. Why, I could read as soon as he could."

This puzzled me yet more: and a thought coming into my head, I asked if he and my father had been twins.

He jumped upon his stool, and the horn spoon fell out of his hand upon the floor. "What gars [= *makes*] ye ask that?" he said, and caught me by the breast of the jacket, and looked this time straight into my eyes: his own, which were little and light, and bright like a bird's, blinking and winking strangely.

"What do you mean?" I asked, very calmly, for I was far stronger than he, and not easily frightened. "Take your hand from my jacket. This is no way to behave."

My uncle seemed to make a great effort upon himself. "Dod, man David," he said, "ye shouldnae speak to me about your father. That's where the mistake is." He sat a while and shook, blinking in his plate: "He was all the brother that ever I had," he added, but with no heart in his voice; and then he caught up his spoon and fell to supper again, but still shaking.

Now this last passage, this laying of hands upon my person and sudden profession of love for my dead father, went so clean beyond my comprehension that it put me into both fear and hope. On the one hand, I began to think my uncle was perhaps insane and might be dangerous; on the other, there came up into my mind (quite unbidden by me and even discouraged) a story like some ballad I had heard folks singing, of a poor lad that was a rightful heir and a wicked kinsman that tired to. keep him from his own. For why should my uncle play a part with a relative that came, almost a beggar, to his door, unless in his heart he had some cause to fear him.

With this notion, all unacknowledged, but nevertheless getting firmly settled in my head, I now began to imitate his covert looks; so that] we sat at table like a cat and a mouse, each stealthily observing the other. Not another word had he to say to me, black or white, but was busy turning something secretly over in his mind; and the longer we sat and the more I looked at him the more certain I became that the something was unfriendly to myself.

When he had cleared the platter, he got out a single pipeful of tobacco, just as in the morning, turned round a stool into the chimney corner, and sat a while smoking, with his back to me.

"Davie," he said at length, "I've been thinking;" then he paused and said it again. "There's a wee bit siller [= *silver*] that I half promised ye before ye were born," he continued; "promised it to your father. O, naething legal, ye understand; just gentlemen daffing at their wine. Well, I keepit that bit money separate — it was a great expense, but a promise is a promise — and it has grown by now to be a maitter of just precisely — just exactly" — and here he paused and stumbled — "of just exactly forty pounds!" This last he rapped out with a sidelong glance over his shoulder; and the next moment added, almost with a scream, "Scots!"

The pound Scots being the same thing as an English shilling, the difference made by this second thought was considerable; I could see, besides, that the whole story was a lie, invented with some end which it puzzled me to guess; and I made no attempt to conceal the tone of raillery in which I answered —

"O, think again, sir! Pounds sterling, I believe!"

"That's what I said," returned my uncle: "pounds sterling! And if you'll step out-by to the door a minute, just to see what kind of a night it is, I'll get it out to ye and call ye in again."

I did his will, smiling to myself in my contempt that he should think I was so easily to be deceived. It was a dark night, with few stars low down; and as I stood just outside the door, I heard a hollow moaning of wind far off among the hills. I said to myself there was something thundery and changeful in the weather, and little knew of what a vast importance that should prove to me before the evening passed.

When I was called in again, my uncle counted out into my hand seven and thirty golden guinea pieces; the rest was in his hand, in small gold and silver; but his heart failed him there and he crammed the change into his pocket.

"There," said he, "that'll show you! I'm a queer man, a strange wi' strangers; but my word is my bond, and there's the proof of it."

Now, my uncle seemed so miserly that I was struck dumb by this sudden generosity, and could find no words in which to thank him.

"No a word!" said he. "Nae thanks; I want nae thanks. I do my duty; I'm no saying that everybody would have done it; but for my part (though I'm a careful body, too) it's a pleasure to me to do the right thing by my brother's son; and it's a pleasure to me to think that now we'll agree as such near friends should."

I spoke him in return as handsomely as I was able; but all the while I was wondering what would come next, and why he had parted with his precious guineas; for as to the reason he had given, a baby would have refused it.

Presently he looked towards me sideways.

"And see here," says he, "tit for tat."

I told him I was ready to prove my gratitude in any reasonable degree, and then waited, looking for some monstrous demand. And yet, when at last he plucked up courage to speak, it was only to tell me (very properly, as I thought) that he was growing old and a little broken, and that he would expect me to help him with the house and the bit garden.

I answered, and expressed my readiness to serve.

"Well," he said, "let's begin." He pulled out of his pocket a rusty key. "There," says he, "there's the key of the stair-tower at the far end of the house. Ye can only win into from the outside, for that part of the house is no finished. Gang ye in there, and up the stairs, and bring me down the chest that's at the top. There's papers in't," he added.

"Can I have a light, sir?" said I.

"Na," said he, very cunningly. "Nae lights in my house."

"Very well, sir," said I. "Are the stairs good?"

"They're grand," said he; and then as I was going, "Keep to the wall," he added; "there's nae bannisters. But the stairs are grand under foot."

Out I went into the night. The wind was still moaning in the distance, though never a breath of it came near the house of Shaws. It had fallen blacker than ever; and I was glad to feel along the wall, till I came the length of the stair-tower door at the far end of the unfinished wing. I had got the key into the keyhole and had just turned it, when all upon a sudden, without sound of wind or thunder, the whole sky lighted up with wild fire and went black again. I had to put my hand over my eyes to get back to the colour of the darkness; and indeed I was already half blinded when I stepped into the tower.

It was so dark inside, it seemed a body could scarce breathe; but I pushed out with foot and hand, and presently struck the wall with the one, and the lowermost round of the stair with the other. The wall, by the touch, was of fine hewn stone; the steps too, though somewhat steep and narrow, were of polished mason work, and regular and solid under foot. Minding my uncle's word about the bannisters, I kept close to the tower side, and felt my way in the pitch darkness with a beating heart.

The house of Shaws stood some five stories high, not counting lofts. Well, as I advanced, it seemed to me the stair grew airier and a thought more lightsome; and I was wondering what might be the cause of this change, when a second blink of the summer lightning came and went. If I did not cry out, it was because fear had me the throat; and if I did not fall, it was more by Heaven's mercy than my own strength. It was not only that the flash shone in on every side through breaches in the wall, so that I seemed to be clambering aloft upon an open scaffold, but the same passing brightness showed me the steps were of unequal length, and that one of my feet rested that moment within two inches of the well.

This was the grand stair! I thought; and with the thought a gust of a kind of angry courage came into my heart. My uncle had sent me here, certainly to run great risks, perhaps to die. I swore I would settle that "perhaps," if I should break my neck for it; got me down upon my hands and knees; and as slowly as a snail, feeling before me every inch, and testing the solidity of every stone, I continued to ascend the stair. The darkness, by contrast with the flash, appeared to have redoubled; nor was that all, for my ears were now troubled and my mind confounded by a great stir of bats in the top part of the tower, and the foul beasts, flying downwards, sometimes beat upon my face and body.

The tower, I should have said, was square; and in every corner the stop was made of a great stone of a different shape, to join the flights. Well, I had come close to one of these turns, when, feeling forward as usual, my hand slipped upon an edge and found nothing but emptiness beyond it. The stair had been carried no higher: to set a stranger mounting it in the darkness was to send him straight to his death; and (although, thanks to the lightning and my own precautions. I was safe enough) the mere thought of the peril in which I might have stood and the dreadful height I might have fallen from, brought out the sweat upon my body and relaxed my joints.

But I knew what I wanted now, and turned and groped my way down again with a wonderful anger in my heart. About half way down, the wind sprang up in a clap and shook the tower, and died again; the rain followed; and before I had reached the ground level it fell in buckets. I put out my head into the storm, and looked along towards the kitchen. The door, which I had shut behind me when I left, now stood open, and shed a little glimmer of light; and I thought I could see a figure standing in the rain, quite still, like a man hearkening. And then there came a blinding flash, which showed me my uncle plainly, just where I had fancied him to stand; and hard upon the heels of it a great tow-row of thunder.

Now, whether my uncle thought the crash to be the sound of my fall, or whether he heard in it God's voice denouncing murder, I will leave you to guess. Certain it is, at least, that he was seized on by a kind of panic fear, and that he ran into the house and left the door open behind him. I followed as softly as I could, and coming unheard into the kitchen, stood and watched him.

He had found time to open the corner cupboard and bring out a great case bottle of aqua vitae, and now sat with his back towards me at the table. Ever and again he would be seized with a fit of deadly shuddering and groan aloud, and carrying the bottle to his lips, drink down the raw spirits by the mouthful.

I stepped forward, came close behind him where he sat, and suddenly clapping my two hands down upon his shoulders — "Ah!" cried I.

My uncle gave a kind of broken cry like a sheeps bleat, flung up his arms, and tumbled to the floor like a dead man. I was somewhat shocked at this; but I had myself to look to first of all, and did not hesitate to let him lie as he had fallen. The keys were hanging in the cupboard; and it was my design to furnish myself with arms before my uncle should come again to his senses and the power of devising evil. In the cupboard were a few bottles, some apparently of medicine; a great many bills and other papers, which I should willingly enough have rummaged, had I had the time; and a few necessaries that were nothing to my purpose. Thence I turned to the chests. The first was full of meal; the second of money-bags and papers tied into sheaves; in the third, with many other things (and these for the most part clothes), I found a rusty, ugly-looking Highland dirk without the scabbard. This, then, I concealed inside my waistcoat, and turned to my uncle.

He lay as he had fallen, all huddled, with one knee up and one arm sprawling abroad; his face had a strange colour of blue, and he seemed to have ceased breathing. Fear came on me that he was dead; then I got water and dashed it in his face; and with that he seemed to come a little to himself, working his mouth and fluttering his eyelids. At last he looked up and saw me, and there came into his eyes a terror that was not of this world.

"Come, come," said I, "sit up."

"Are you alive?" he sobbed. "O man, are ye alive?"

"That am I," said I. "Small thanks to you!"

He had begun to seek for his breath with deep sighs. "The blue phial," said he — "in the aumry [= *dresser*] — the blue phial." His breath came slower still.

I ran to the cupboard, and, sure enough, found there a blue phial of medicine, with the dose written on it on a paper, and this I administered to him with what speed I might.

"It's the trouble," said he, reviving a little; "I have a trouble, Davie. It's the heart."

I set him on a chair and looked at him. It is true I felt some pity for a man that looked so sick, but I was full besides of righteous anger; and I numbered over before him the points on which I wanted explanation: Why he lied to me at every word; [why he feared that I should leave him; why he disliked it to be hinted that he and my father were twins — "Is that because it is true?" I asked;] why he had given me money to which I was convinced I had no claim; and, last of all, why he had tried to kill me. He heard me all through in silence; and then, in a broken voice, begged me to let him go to bed.

"I'll tell ye the morn," he said; "as sure as death I will."

And so weak was he that I could do nothing but consent. I locked him into his room, however, and pocketed the key; and then returning to the kitchen, made up such a blaze as had not shone there for many a long year, and, wrapping myself in my plaid, lay down upon the chests and fell asleep.

● *Children begin by loving their parents; after a time they judge them; rarely, if ever, do they forgive them.*

(Oscar Wilde)

HOP-FROG
by Edgar Allan Poe   **19**
                                                           [17]

I never knew any one so keenly alive to a joke as the king was. He seemed
to live only for joking. To tell a good story of the joke kind, and to tell it
well, was the surest road to his favour. Thus it happened that his seven
ministers were all noted for their accomplishments as jokers. They all took
after the king, too, in being large, corpulent, oily men, as well as inimitable
jokers. [Whether people grow fat by joking, or whether there is something in
fat itself which predisposes to a joke, I have never been quite able to
determine; but certain it is that a lean joker is a *rara avis in terris.*

About the refinements, or, as he called them, the "ghosts" of wit, the king
troubled himself very little. He had an especial admiration for *breadth* in a
jest, and would often put up with *length*, for the sake of it. Over-niceties
wearied him. He would have preferred Rabelais's *Gargantua* to the *Zadig* of
Voltaire: and, upon the whole, practical jokes suited his taste far better than
verbal ones.

At the date of my narrative, professing jesters had not altogether gone out
of fashion at court. Several of the great continental "powers" still retained
their "fools," who wore motley, with caps and bells, and who were expected
to be always ready with sharp witticisms, at a moment's notice, in
consideration of the crumbs that fell from the royal table.]

Our king, as a matter of course, retained his "fool." The fact is, he
required something in the way of folly — if only to counterbalance the heavy
wisdom of the seven wise men who were his ministers — not to mention
himself.

His fool, or professional jester, was not *only* a fool, however,. His value
was trebled in the eyes of the king by the fact of his being also a dwarf and a
cripple. Dwarfs were as common at court, in those days, as fools; and many
monarchs would have found it difficult to get through their days (days are
rather longer at court than elsewhere) without both a jester to laugh *with*,
and a dwarf to laugh *at*. [But, as I have already observed, your jesters, in
ninety-nine cases out of a hundred, are fat, round, and unwieldy — so that it
was no small source of self-gratulation with our king that, in Hop-Frog (this
was the fool's name) he possessed a triplicate treasure in one person.]

I believe the name "Hop-Frog" was *not* that given to the dwarf by his sponsors at baptism, but it was conferred upon him, by general consent of the seven ministers, on account of his inability to walk as other men do. In fact, Hop-Frog could only get along by [a sort of interjectional gait —] something between a leap and a wriggle — a movement that afforded illimitable amusement, and of course consolation, to the king, [for (notwithstanding the protuberance of his stomach and a consitutional swelling of the head) the king, by his whole court, was accounted a capital figure.]

But although Hop-Frog, through the distortion of his legs, could move only with great pain and difficulty along a road or floor, the prodigious muscular power which nature seemed to have bestowed upon his arms, by way of compensation for deficiency in the lower limbs, enabled him to perform many feats of wonderful dexterity, where trees or ropes were in question, or anything else to climb. At such exercises he certainly much more resembled a squirrel, or a small monkey, than a frog.

I am not able to say, with precision, from what country Hop-Frog originally came. It was from some barbarous region, however, that no person ever heard of — a vast distance from the court of our king. Hop-Frog, and a young girl from little less dwarfish than himself (although of exquisiste proportions, and a marvellous dancer), had been forcibly carried off from their respective homes in adjoining provinces, and sent as presents to the king, by one of his ever-victorious generals.

Under these circumstances, it is not be wondered at that a close intimacy arose between the two little captives. Indeed, they soon became sworn friends. Hop-Frog, who, although he made a great deal of sport, was by no means popular, had it not in his power to render Trippetta many services; but *she*, on account of her grace and exquisite beauty (although a dwarf), was universally admired and petted: so she possessed much influence; and never failed to use it, whenever she could, for the benefit of Hop-Frog.

On some grand state occasion — I forget what — the king determined to have a masquerade; and whenever a. masquerade, or anything of that kind, occurred at our court, then the talents both of Hop-Frog, in especial, was so inventive in the way of getting up pageants, suggesting novel characters and arranging costume for masked balls, that nothing could be done, it seems, without his assistance.

The night appointed for the *fête* had arrived. A gorgeous hall had been fitted up, under Trippetta's eye, with every kind of device which could possibly give *éclat* [= *high style*] to a masquerade. The whole court was in a fever of expectation. As for costumes and characters, it might well be

F

supposed that everybody had come to a decision on such points. Many had made up their minds as to what *rôles* they should assume, a week, or even a month, in advance; and, in fact, there was not a particle of indecision anywhere – except in the case of the King and his seven ministers. Why *they* hesitated I never could tell, unless they did it by way of a joke. More probably, they found it difficult, on account of being so fat, to make up their minds. At all events, time flew; and, as a last resource, they sent for Trippetta and Hop-Frog

When the two little friends obeyed the summons of the king, they found him sitting at his wine with the seven members of his cabinet council; but the monarch appeared to be in a very ill humour. He knew that Hop-Frog was not fond of wine; for it excited the poor cripple almost to madness; and madness is no comfortable feeling. But the king loved his practical jokes, and took pleasure in forcing Hop-Frog to drink and (as the king called it) "to be merry."

"Come here, Hop-Frog," said he, as the jester and his friend entered the room: "swallow this bumper to the health of your absent friends" (here Hop-Frog sighed), "and then let us have the benefit of your invention. We want characters – *characters*, man – something novel – out of the way. We are wearied with this everlasting sameness. Come, drink! the wine will brighten your wits."

Hop-Frog endeavoured, as usual, to get up a jest in reply to these advances from the king; but the effort was too much. It happened to be the poor dwarf's birthday, and the command to drink to his "absent friends" forced the tears to his eyes. Many large, bitter drops fell into the goblet as he took it, humbly, from the hand of the tyrant.

"Ah! ha! ha! ha!" roared the latter, as the dwarf reluctantly drained the beaker. "See what a glass of good wine can do! Why, your eyes are shining already!"

Poor fellow! his large eyes *gleamed* rather than shone, for the effect of wine on his excitable brain was not more powerful than instantaneous. He placed the goblet nervously on the table, and looked round upon the company with a half-insane stare. They all seemed highly amused at the success of the King's "*joke*."

"And now to business," said the prime minister, a *very* fat man.

"Yes," said the king; "come, Hop-Frog, lend us your assistance. Characters, my fine fellow; we stand in need of characters – all of us – ha! ha! ha!" and as this was seriously meant for a joke, his laugh was chorused by the seven.

Hop-Frog also laughed, although feebly and somewhat vacantly.

"Come, come," said the king, impatiently, "have you nothing to suggest?"

"I am endeavouring to think of something *novel*," replied the dwarf, abstractedly, for he was quite bewildered by the wine.

"Endeavouring!" cried the tyrant, fiercely; "what do you mean by *that*? Ah, I perceive. You are sulky and want more wine. Here, drink this!" and he poured out another gobletful and offered to the cripple, who merely gazed at it, gasping for breath.

"Drink, I say!" shouted the monster, "or by the fiends—"

The dwarf hesitated. The king grew purple with rage. The courtiers smirked. Trippetta, pale as a corpse, advanced to the monarch's seat, and, falling on her knees before him, implored him to spare her friend.

The tyrant regarded her, for some moments, in evident wonder at her audacity. He seemed quite at a loss what to do or say — how most becomingly to express his indignation. At last, without uttering a syllable, he pushed her violently from him, and threw the contents of the brimming goblet in her face.

The poor girl got up as best she could, and, not daring even to sigh, resumed her position at the foot of the table.

There was a dead silence for about half a minute, during which the falling of a leaf, or of a feather, might have been heard. It was interrupted by a low, but harsh and protracted *grating* sound which seemed to come at once from every corner of the room.

"What—what—*what*— are you making that noise for?" demanded the king, turning furiously to the dwarf.

The latter seemd to have recovered, in great measure, from his intoxication, and looked fixedly but quietly into the tyrant's face, merely ejaculated:

"I—I? How could it have been me?"

"The sound appeared to come from without," observed one of the courtiers. "I fancy it was the parrot at the window, whetting his bill upon his cage-wires."

"True," replied the monarch, as if much relieved by the suggestion; "but, on the honour of a knight, I could have sworn that it was the gritting of this vagabond's teeth."

Hereupon the dwarf laughed (the king was too confirmed a joker to object to any one's laughing), and displayed a set of large, powerful, and very repulsive teeth. Moreover, he avowed his perfect willingness to swallow as much wine as desired. The monarch was pacified; and having drained another bumper with no very perceptible ill effect, Hop-Frog entered at once, and with spirit, into the plans for the masquerade.

"I cannot tell what was the association of idea," observed he, very tranquilly, and as if he had never tasted wine in his life, "but *just after* you had struck the girl and thrown the wine in her face – *just after* your majesty had done this, and while the parrot was making that odd noise outside the window, there came into my mind a capital diversion – one of my own country frolics – often enacted among us, at our masquerades: but here it will be new altogether. Unfortunately, however, it requires a company of eight persons, and –"

"Here we *are*!" cried the king, laughing at his acute discovering of the coincidence; "eight to a fraction – I and my seven ministers. Come! what is the diversion?"

"We call it," replied the cripple, "the Eight Chained Ourang-Outangs, and it really is excellent sport if well enacted."

"*We* will enact it," remarked the king, drawing himself up, and lowering her eyelids.

"The beauty of the game," continued Hop-Frog, "lies in the fright it occasions among the women."

"Capital!" roared in chorus the monarch and his ministry.

"I will equip you as ourang-outangs," proceeded the dwarf; "leave all that to me. The resemblance shall be so striking that the company of masqueraders will take you for real beasts – and, of course, they will be as much terrified as astonished."

"Oh, this is exquisite!" exclaimed the king. "Hop-Frog! I will make a man of you."

"The chains are for the purpose of increasing the confusion by their jangling. You are supposed to have escaped, *en masse*, from your keepers. Your majesty cannot conceive the *effect* produced, at a masquerade, by eight chained ourang-outangs, imagined to be real ones by most of the company, and rushing in with savage cries among the crowd of delicately and gorgeously habited men and women. The *contrast* is inimitable."

"It *must* be," said the king: and the council arose hurriedly (as it was growing late), to put in execution the scheme of Hog-Frog.

His mode of equipping the party as ourang-outangs was very simple, but effective enough for his purposes. [The animals in question had, at the epoch of my story, very rarely been seen in any part of the civilised world; and as the imitations made by the dwarf were sufficiently beast-like and more than sufficiently hideous, their truthfulness to nature was thus thought to be secured.]

The king and his ministers were first encased in tight-fitting stockinette shirts and drawers. They were then saturated with tar. At this stage of the process, some one of the party suggested feathers; but the suggestion was at once overruled by the dwarf, who soon convinced the eight, by ocular [= *visible*] demonstration, that the hair of such a brute as the ourang-outrang was much more efficiently represented by *flax*. A thick coating of the latter was accordingly plastered upon the coating of tar. A long chain was now procured. First, it was passed about the waist of the king, *and tied*; then about another of the party, and also tied; then about all successively, in the same manner. When this chaining arrangement was complete, and the party stood as far apart from each other as possible, they formed a circle; and to make all things appear natural. Hop-Frog passed the residue of the chain, in two diameters, at right angles, across the circle, after the fashion adopted, at the present day, by those who capture Chimpanzees, or other large apes, in Borneo.

The grand saloon in which the masquerade was to take place, was a circular room, very lofty, and receiving the light of the sun only through a single window at top. At night (the season for which the apartment was especially designed), it was illuminated principally by a large chandelier, depending by a chain from the centre of the sky-light, and lowered, or elevated, by means of a counterbalance as usual; but (in order not to look unsightly) this latter passed outside the cupola over the roof.

The arrangements of the room had been left to Trippetta's superintendence; but, in some particulars, it seems, she had been guided by the calmer judgement of her friend the dwarf. At his suggestion it was that, on this occasion, the chandelier was removed. Its waxen drippings (which, in weather so warm, it was quite impossible to prevent) would have been seriously detrimental to the rich dresses of the guests, who, on account of the crowded state of the saloon, could not *all* be expected to keep from out its centre — that is to say, from under the chandelier. Additional sconces were set in various parts of the hall, out of the way; and a flambeau, [= *torch*] emitting sweet odour was placed in the right hand of each of the Caryatides [= *statues*] that stood against the wall — some fifty or sixty altogether.

The eight ourang-outangs, taking Hop-Frog's advice, waited patiently until midnight (when the room was thoroughly filled with masqueraders) before making their appearance. No sooner had the clock ceased striking, however, then they rushed, or rather rolled in, all together − for the impediment of their chains caused most of the party to fall, and all to stumble as they entered.

The excitement among the masqueraders was prodigious, and filled the heart of the king with glee. As had been anticipated, there were not a few of the guests who supposed the ferocious-looking creatures to be beasts of *some* kind in reality, if not precisely ourang-outangs. Many of the women swooned with affright; and had not the king taken the precaution to exclude all weapons from the saloon, his party might soon have expiated their frolic in their blood. As it was, a general rush was made for the doors; but the king had ordered them to be locked immediately upon his entrance; and, at the dwarf's suggestion, the keys had been deposited with *him*.

While the tumult was at its height, and each masquerader attentive only to his own safety (for, in fact, there was much *real* danger from the pressure of the excited crowd), the chain by which the chandelier ordinarily hung, and which had been drawn up on its removal, might have been seen very gradually to descend, until its hooked extremity came within three feet of the floor.

Soon after this, the king and his seven friends, having reeled about the hall in all direction, found themselves, at length, in its centre, and, of course, in immediate contact with the chain. While they were thus situated, the dwarf, who had followed closely at their heels, inciting them to keep up the commotion, took hold of their own chain at the intersection of the two portions which crossed the circle diametrically and at right angles. Here, with the rapidity of thought, he inserted the hook from which the chandelier had been wont to depend; and, in an instant, by some unseen agency, the chandelier-chain was drawn so far upward as to take the hook out of reach, and, as an inevitable consequence, to drag the ourang-outangs together in close connection, and face to face.

The masqueraders, by this time, had recovered, in some measure, from their alarm; beginning to regard the whole matter as a well-contrived pleasantry, set up a loud shout of laughter at the predicament of the apes.

"Leave them to *me*!" now screamed Hop-Frog, his shrill voice making itself easily heard through all the din. "Leave them to *me*. I fancy *I* know them. If I can only get a good look at them, *I* can soon tell who they are."

Here, scrambling over the heads of the crowd, he managed to get to the wall; when, seizing a flambeau from one of the Caryatides [= *statues*], he returned, as he went, to the centre of the room − leaped, with the agility of a monkey, upon the king's head — and thence clambered a few feet up the chain — holding down the torch to examine the group of ourang-outangs, and still screaming, "*I* shall soon find out who they are!"

And now, while the whole assembly (the apes included) were convulsed with laughter, the jester suddenly uttered a shrill whistle; when the chain flew violently up for about thirty feet — dragging with it the dismayed and struggling ourang-outans, and leaving them suspended in mid-air between the sky-light and the floor. Hop-Frog, clinging to the chain as it rose, still maintained his relative position in respect to the eight maskers, and still (as if nothing were the matter) continued to thrust his torch down towards them, as though endeavouring to discover who they were.

So thoroughly astonished were the whole company at this ascent, that a dead silence, of about a minute's duration, ensued. It was broken by just such a low, harsh, *grating* sound, as had before attracted the attention of the king and his councillors, when the former threw the wine in the face of Trippetta. But, on the present occasion, there could be no question as to *whence* the sound issued. It came from the fang-like teeth of the dwarf, who ground them and gnashed them as he foamed at the mouth, and glared, with an expression of maniacal rage, into the upturned countenances of the king and his seven companions.

"Ah, ha!" said at length the infuriated jester. "Ah, ha! I begin to see who these people *are*, now!" Here, pretending to scrutinise the king more closely, he held the flambeaut to the flaxen coat which enveloped him, and which instantly burst into a sheet of vivid flame. In less than half a minute the whole eight ourang-outangs were blazing fiercely, amid the shrieks of the multitude who gazed at them from below, horror-stricken, and without the power to render them the slightest assistance.

At length the flames, suddenly increasing in virulence, forced the jester to climb higher up the chain, to be out of their reach; and, as he made this movement, the crowd again sank, for a brief instant, into silence. The dwarf seized his opportunity, and once more spoke:

"I now see *distinctly*," he said, "what manner of people these maskers are. They are a great king and his seven privy-councillors — a king who does not scruple to strike a defenceless girl, and his seven councillors who abet him in the outrage. As for myself, I am simply Hop-Frog, the jester — and *this is my last jest*."

Owing to the high combustibility of both the flax and the tar to which it adhered, the dwarf had scarcely made an end of his brief speech before the work of vengeance was complete. The eight corpses swung in their chains, a fetid, blackened, hideous, and indistinguishable mass. The cripple hurled his torch at them, clambered leisurely to the ceiling, and disappeared through the sky-light.

It is supposed that Trippetta, stationed on the roof of the saloon, had been the accomplice of her friend in his fiery revenge, and that, together, they effected their escape to their own country: for neither was seen again.

THE STRIPED CHEST

by Sir A. Conan Doyle   27
                                                    [24½]

"What do you make of her, Allardyce?" I asked.

My second mate was standing beside me upon the poop, with his short, thick legs astretch, for the gale had left a considerable swell behind it, and our two quarter-boats nearly touched the water with every roll. He steadied his glass against the mizzen-shrouds, and he looked long and hard at this disconsolate stranger every time she came reeling up on to the crest of a roller and hung balanced for a few seconds before swooping down upon the other side. She lay so low in the water that I could only catch an occasional glimpse of a pea-green line of bulwark.

She was a brig, but her mainmast had been snapped short off some ten feet above the deck, and no effort seemed to have been made to cut away the wreckage, which floated, sails and yards, like the broken wing of a wounded gull, upon the water beside her. The fore-mast was still standing, but the fore-topsail was flying loose, and the headsails were streaming out in long white pennons in front of her. Never have I seen a vessel which appeared to have gone through rougher handling.

But we could not be surprised at that, for there had been times during the last three days when it was a question whether our own barque would ever see land again. For thirty-six hours we had kept her nose to it, and if the *Mary Sinclair* had not been as good a seaboat as ever left the Clyde, we could not have gone through. And yet here we were at the end of it with the loss only of our gig and of part of the starboard bulwark. It did not astonish us, however, when the smother had cleared away, to find that others had been less lucky, and that this mutilated brig, staggering about upon a blue sea, and under a cloudless sky, had been left, like a blinded man after a lightning flash, to tell of the terror which is past.

[Allardyce, who was a slow and methodical Scotchman, stared long and hard at the little craft, while our seamen lined the bulwark, or clustered upon the fore shrouds to have a view of the stranger. In latitude 20° and longitude 10°, which were about our bearings, one becomes a little curious as to whom one meets, for one has left the main lines of Atlantic commerce to the north. For ten days we had been sailing over a solitary sea.]

"She's derelict, I'm thinking," said the second mate.

I had come to the same conclusion, for I could see no sign of life upon her deck, and there was no answer to the friendly wavings from our seamen. The crew had probably deserted her under the impression that she was about to founder.

"She can't last long," continued Allardyce, in his measured way. "She may put her nose down and her tail up any minute. The water's lipping up to the edge of her rail."

["What's her flag?" I asked.

"I'm trying to make out. It's got all twisted and tangled with the halyards. Yes. I've got it now, clear enough. It's the Brazilian flag, but it's wrong side up."

She had hoisted a signal of distress, then, before her people had abandoned her. Perhaps they had only just gone. I took the mate's glass and looked round over the tumultuous face of the deep blue Atlantic, still veined and starred with white lines and spoutings of foam. But nowhere could I see anything human beyond ourselves.]

"There may be living men aboard," said I.

"There may be salvage," muttered the second mate.

"Then we will run down upon her lee side, and lie to."

We were not more than a hundred yards from her when we swung our foreyard aback, and there we were, the barque and the brig, ducking and bowing like two clowns in a dance.

"Drop one of the quarter-boats," said I. "Take four men, Mr. Allardyce, and see what you can learn of her."

But just at that moment my first officer, Mr. Armstrong, came on deck, for seven bells had struck, and it was but a few minutes off his watch. It would interest me to go myself to this abandoned vessel and to see what there might be aboard of her. So, with a word to Armstrong, I swung myself over the side, slipped down the falls, and took my place in the sheets of the boat.

It was but a little distance, but it took some time to traverse, and so heavy was the roll, that often, when we were in the trough of the sea, we could not see either the barque which we had left or the brig which we were approaching. The sinking sun did not penetrate down there, and it was cold and dark in the hollows of the waves, but each passing billow heaved us up into the warmth and the sunshine once more. At each of these moments, as we hung upon a white-capped ridge between the two dark valleys, I caught a glimpse of the long, pea-green line, and the nodding foremast of the brig, and I steered so as to come round by her stern, so that we might determine which was the best way of boarding her. As we passed her we saw the name *Nossa Sehnora da Vittoria* painted across her dripping counter.

"The weather side, sir," said the second mate. "Stand by with the boathook, carpenter!" An instant later we had jumped over the bulwarks, which were hardly higher that our boat, and found ourselves upon the deck of the abandoned vessel.

[Our first thought was to provide for our own safety in case — as seemed very probable — the vessel should settle down beneath our feet. With this object two of our men held on to the painter of the boat, and fended her off from the vessel's side, so that she might be ready in case we had to make a hurried retreat. The carpenter was sent to find out how much water there was, and whether it was still gaining, while the other seaman, Allardyce and myself, made a rapid inspection of the vessel and her cargo.]

The deck was littered with wreckage and with hen-coops, in which the dead birds were washing about. The boats were gone, with the exception of one, the bottom of which had been stove, and it was certain that the crew had abandoned the vessel. The cabin was in a deck house, one side of which had been beaten in by a heavy sea. Allardyce and I entered it, and found the captain's table as he had left it, his books and papers — all Spanish or Portuguese — scattered over it, with piles of cigarette ash everywhere. I looked about for the log, but could not find it.

"As likely as not he never kept one," said Allardyce. "Things are pretty slack aboard a South American trader, and they don't do more than they can help. If there was one it must have been taken away with him in the boat."

"I should like to take all these books and papers," said I. "Ask the carpenter how much time we have."

His report was reassuring. The vessel was full of water, but some of the cargo was buoyant, and there was no immediate danger of her sinking. Probably she would never sink, but would drift as one of those terrible, unmarked reefs which have sent so many stout vessels to the bottom.

"In that case there is no danger in your going below, Mr. Allardyce," said I. "See what you can make of her, and find out how much of her cargo may be saved. I'll look through these papers while you are gone."

The bills of lading, and some notes and letters which lay upon the desk, sufficed to inform me that the Brazilian brig *Nossa Sehnora da Vittoria* had cleared from Bahia a month before. The name of the captain was Texeira, but there was no record as the number of the crew. She was bound for London, and a glance at the bills of lading was sufficient to show me that we were not likely to profit much in the way of salvage. [Her cargo consisted of nuts, ginger, and wood, the latter in the shape of great logs of valuable tropical growths. It was these, no doubt, which had prevented the ill-fated vessel from going to the bottom, but they were of such a size as to make it impossible for us to extract them. Besides these, there were a few fancy goods, such as a number of ornamental birds for millinery purposes, and a hundred cases of preserved fruits.] And then, as I turned over the papers, I came upon a short note in English, which arrested my attention.

"It is requested," said the note, "that the various old Spanish and Indian curiosities, which came out of the Santarem collection, and which are consigned to Prontfoot and Neuman, of Oxford Street, London, should be put in some place where there may be no danger of these very valuable and unique articles being injured or tampered with. This applies most particularly to the treasure-chest of Don Ramirez di Leyra, which must on no account be placed where anyone can get at it."

The treasure-chest of Don Ramirez! Unique and valuable articles! Here was a chance of salvage after all! I had risen to my feet with the paper in my hand, when my Scotch mate appeared in the doorway.

"I'm thinking all isn't quite as it should be aboard of this ship, sir," said he. He was a hard-faced man, and yet I could see that he had been startled.

"What's the matter?"

"Murder's the matter, sir. There's a man here with his brains beaten out."

"Killed in the storm?" said I.

"Maybe so, sir. But I'll be surprised if you think so after you have seen him."

"Where is he, then?"

"This way, sir; here in the main-deck house."

There appeared to have been no accommodation below in the brig, for there was the afterhouse for the captain, another by the main hatchway with the cook's galley attached to it, and a third in the forecastle for the men. It was to this middle one that the mate led me. As you entered, the galley, with its litter of tumbled pots and dishes, was upon the right, and upon the left was a small room with two bunks for the officers. Then beyond there was a place about twelve feet square, which was littered with flags and spare canvas. All round the walls were a number of packets done up in coarse cloth and carefully lashed to the woodwork. At the other end was a great box, striped red and white, though the red was so faded and the white so dirty that it was only where the light fell directly upon it that one could see the colouring. The box was, by subsequent measurement, four feet three inches in length, three feet two inches in height, and three feet across — considerably larger than a seaman's chest.

But it was not to the box that my eyes or my thoughts were turned as I entered the store-room. On the floor, lying across the litter of bunting, there was stretch a small, dark man with a short, curling beard. He lay as far as it was possible from the box, with his feet towards it and his head away. A crimson patch was printed upon the white canvas on which his head was resting, and little red ribbons wreathed themselves round his swarthy neck and trailed away on to the floor, but there was no sign of a wound that I could see, and his face was as placid as that of a sleeping child.

It was only when I stooped that I could perceive his injury, and then I turned away with an exclamation of horror. He had been pole-axed; apparently by some person standing behind him. A frightful blow had smashed in the top of his head and penetrated deeply into his brain. His face might well be placid, for death must have been absolutely instantaneous, and the position of the wound showed that he could never have seen the person who had inflicted it.

"Is that foul play or accident, Captain Barclay?" asked my second mate, demurely.

"You are quite right, Mr. Allardyce. The man has been murdered, struck down from above by a sharp and heavy weapon. But who was he, and why did they murder him?"

"He was a common seaman, sir," said the mate. "You can see that if you look at his fingers." He turned out his pockets as he spoke and brought to light a pack of cards, some tarred string, and a bundle of Brazilian tobacco.

"Hullo, look at this!" said he.

It was a large, open knife with a stiff spring blade which he had picked up from the floor. The steel was shining and bright, so that we could not associate it with the crime, and yet the dead man had apparently held it in his hand when he was struck down, for it still lay within his grasp.

"It looks to me, sir, as if he knew he was in danger, and kept his knife handy," said the mate. "However, we can't help the poor beggar now. I can't make out these things that are lashed to the wall. They seem to be idols and weapons and curios of all sorts done up in old sacking."

"That's right," said I. "They are the only things of value that we are likely to get from the cargo. Hail the barque and tell them to send the other quarter-boat to help us to get the stuff aboard."

While he was away I examined this curious plunder which had come into our possession. The curiosities were so wrapped up that I could only form a general idea as to their nature, but the striped box stood in a good light where I could thoroughly examine it. On the lid, which was clamped and cornered with metal-work, there was engraved a complex coat of arms, and beneath it was a line of Spanish which I was able to decipher as meaning, "The treasure-chest of Don Ramirez di Leyra, Knight of the Order of Saint James, Governor and Captain-General of Terra Firma and of the Province of Veraquas." In one corner was the date 1606, and on the other a large white label, upon which was written in English, "You are earnestly requested, upon no account, to open this box." The same warning was repeated underneath in Spanish. As to the lock, it was a very complex and heavy one of engraved steel, with a Latin motto, which was above a seaman's comprehension.

By the time I had finished this examination of the peculiar box, the other quarter-boat with Mr. Armstrong, the first officer, had come alongside, and we began to carry out and place in her the various curiosities which appeared to be the only objects worth moving from the derelict ship. When she was full I sent her back to the barque, and then Allardyce and I, with a carpenter and one seaman, shifted the striped box, which was the only thing left, to our boat, and lowered it over, balancing it upon the two middle thwarts, for it was so heavy that it would have given the boat a dangerous tilt had we placed it at either end. As to the dead man, we left him where we had found him.

The mate had a theory that, at the moment of the desertion of the ship, this fellow had started plundering, and that the captain in an attempt to preserve discipline, had struck him down with a hatchet or some other heavy weapon. It seemed more probable than any other explanation, and yet it did not entirely satisfy me either. But the ocean is full of mysteries, and we were content to leave the fate of the dead seaman of the Brazilian brig to be added to that long list which every sailor can recall.

The heavy box was slung up by ropes on to the deck of the *Mary Sinclair*, and was carried by four seamen into the cabin, where, between the table and the afterlockers, there was just space for it to stand. There it remained during supper, and after that meal the mates remained with me, and discussed over a glass of grog the event of the day. Mr. Armstrong was a long, thin, vulture-like man, an excellent seaman, but famous for his nearness and cupidity [= *greed*]. Our treasure-trove had excited him greatly, and already he had begun with glistening eyes to reckon up how much it might be worth to each of us when the shares of the salvage came to be divided.

"If the paper said that they were unique, Mr. Barclay, then they may be worth anything that you like to name. You wouldn't believe the sums that the rich collectors give. A thousand pounds is nothing to them. We'll have something to show for our voyage, or I am mistaken."

"I don't think that," said I. "As far as I can see they are not very different from any other South American curios."

"Well, sir, I've traded there for fourteen voyages, and I have never seen anything like that chest before. That's worth a pile of money, just as it stands. But it's so heavy, that surely there must be something valuable inside it. Don't you think we ought to open it and see?"

"If you break it open you will spoil it, as likely as not," said the second mate.

Armstrong squatted down in front of it, with his head on one side, and his long, thin nose within a few inches of the lock.

"The wood is oak," said he, "and it has shrunk a little with age. If I had a chisel or a strong-bladed knife I could force the lock back without doing any damage at all."

The mention of a strong-bladed knife made me think of the dead seaman upon the brig.

"I wonder if he could have been on the job when someone came to interfere with him," said I.

"I don't know about that, sir, but I am perfectly certain I could open the box. There's a screw-driver here in the locker. Just hold the lamp, Allardyce, and I'll have it done in a brace of shakes."

"Wait a bit," said I, for already, with eyes which gleamed with curiosity and with avarice, he was stooping over the lid. "I don't see that there is any hurry over this matter. You've read that card which warns us not to open it.

It may mean anything or it may mean nothing, but somehow I feel inclined to obey it. After all, whatever is in it will keep, and if it is valuable it will be worth as much if it is opened in the owner's offices as in the cabin of the *Mary Sinclair*."

[The first officer seemed bitterly disappointed at my decision.

"Surely, sir, you are not superstitious about it," said he, with a slight sneer upon his thin lips. "If it gets out of our own hands, and we don't see for ourselves what is inside it, we may be done out of our rights; besides —"

"That's enough, Mr. Armstrong," said I, abruptly. "You may have every confidence that you will get your rights, but I will not have that box opened to-night."

"Why, the label itself shows that the box has been examined by Europeans," Allardyce added. "Because a box is a treasure-box is no reason that it has treasures inside it now. A good many folk have had a peep into it since the days of the old Governor of Terra Firma."]

Armstrong threw the screwdriver down upon the table and shrugged his shoulders.

"Just as you like," said he; but for the rest of the evening, although we spoke upon many subjects, I noticed that his eyes were continually coming round, with the same expression of curiosity and greed, to the old striped box.

And now I come to that portion of my story which fills me even now with a shuddering horror when I think of it. The main cabin had the rooms of the officers round it, but mine was the farthest away from it at the end of the little passage which led to the companion. No regular watch was kept by me, except in cases of emergency, and the three mates divided the watches among them. Armstrong had the middle watch, which ends at four in the morning, and he was relieved by Allardyce. For my part I have always been one of the soundest of sleepers, and it is rare for anything less than a hand upon my shoulder to arouse me.

And yet I was aroused that night, or rather in the early grey of the morning. It was just half-past four by my chronometer when something caused me to sit up in my berth wide awake and with every nerve tingling. It was a sound of some sort, a crash with a human cry at the end of it, which still jarred upon my ears. I sat listening, but all was now silent. And yet it could not have been imagination, that hideous cry, for the echo of it still rang in my head, and it seemed to have come from some place quite close to me. I sprang from my bunk, and, pulling on some clothes, I made my way into the cabin.

At first I saw nothing unusual there. In the cold, grey light I made out the red-clothed table, the six rotating chairs, the walnut lockers, the swinging barometer, and there, at the end, the big striped chest. I was turning away with the intention of going upon deck and asking the second mate if he had heard anything when my eyes fell suddenly upon something which projected from under the table. It was the leg of a man − a leg with a long sea-boot upon it. I stooped, and there was a figure sprawling upon his face, his arms thrown forward and his body twisted. Once glance told me that it was Armstrong, the first officer, and a second that he was a dead man. For a few moments I stood gasping. Then I rushed on to the deck, called Allardyce to my assistance, and came back with him into the cabin.

Together we pulled the unfortunate fellow from under the table, and as we looked at his dripping head we exchanged glances, and I do not know which was the paler of the two.

"The same as the Spanish sailor," said I.

"The very same. God preserve us! It's that infernal chest! Look at Armstrong's hand!"

He held up the mate's right hand, and there was the screwdriver which he had wished to use the night before.

"He's been at the chest, sir. He knew that I was on deck and you asleep. He knelt down in front of it, and he pushed the lock back with that tool. Then something happened to him and he cried out so that you heard him."

"Allardyce," I whispered, "what *could* have happened to him?"

The second mate put his hand upon my sleeve and drew me into his cabin.

"We can talk here, sir, and we don't know who may be listening to us in there. What do you suppose is in that box, Captain Barclay?"

"I give you my word, Allardyce, that I have no idea."

"Well, I can only find one theory which will fit all the facts. Look at the size of the box. Look at all the carving and metal-work which may conceal any number of holes. Look at the weight of it; it took four men to carry it. On the top of that, remember that two men have tried to open it, and both have come to their end through it. Now, sir, what can it mean except one thing?"

"You mean there is a man in it?"

"Of course there is a man in it. You know how it is in these South American States, sir. A man may be President one week and hunted like a dog the next. They are for ever flying for their lives. My idea is that there is some fellow in hiding there, who is armed and desperate, and who will fight to the death before he is taken."

"But his food and drink?"

"It's a roomy chest, sir, and he may have some provisions stowed away. As to his drink, he had a friend among the crew upon the brig who saw that he had what he needed."

"You think, then, that the label asking people not to open the box was simply written in his interest?"

"Yes, sir, that is my idea. Have you any other way of explaining the facts?"

I had to confess that I had not.

"The question is what are we to do?" I asked.

"The man's a dangerous ruffian who sticks at nothing. I'm thinking it wouldn't be a bad thing to put a rope round the chest and tow it alongside for half an hour; when we could open it at our ease. Or if we just tied the box up and kept him from getting any water maybe that would do as well. Or the carpenter could put a coat of varnish over it and stop all the blowholes."

"Come, Allardyce," said I, angrily. "You don't seriously mean to say that a whole ship's company are going to be terrorized by a single man in a box. If he's there, I'll engage to fetch him out!" I went to my room and came back with my revolver in my hand. "Now, Allardyce," said I. "Do you open the lock, and I'll stand on guard."

"For God's sake, think what you are doing, sir!" cried the mate. "Two men have lost their lives over it, and the blood of one not yet dry upon the carpet."

"The more reason why we should revenge him."

"Well, sir, at least let me call the carpenter. Three are better than two, and he is a good stout man."

He went off in search of him, and I was left alone with the striped chest in the cabin. I don't think that I'm a nervous man, but I kept the table between me and this solid old relic of the Spanish Main. In the growing light of morning the red and white striping was beginning to appear, and the curious scrolls and wreaths of metal and carving which showed the loving pains which cunning craftsmen had expended upon it. Presently the carpenter and the mate came back together, the former with a hammer in his hand.

"It's a bad business, this, sir," said he, shaking his head, as he looked at the body of the mate. "And you think there's someone hiding in the box?"

"There's no doubt about it," said Allardyce, picking up the screwdriver and setting his jaw like a man who needs to brace his courage. "I'll drive the lock back if you will both stand by. If he rises let him have it on the head with your hammer, carpenter! Shoot at once, sir, if he raises his hand. Now!"

He had knelt down in front of the striped chest, and passed the blade of the tool under the lid. With a sharp snick the lock flew back. "Stand by!" yelled the mate, and with a heave he threw open the massive top of the box. As it swung up, we all three sprang back, I with my pistol levelled, and the carpenter with the hammer above his head. Then, as nothing happened, we each took a step forward and peeped in. The box was empty.

Not quite empty either, for in one corner was lying an old yellow candlestick, elaborately engraved, which appeared to be as old as the box itself. Its rich yellow tone and artistic shape suggested that it was an object of value. For the rest there was nothing more weighty or valuable than dust in the old striped treasure-chest.

"Well, I'm blessed!" cried Allardyce, staring blankly into it. "Where does the weight come in, then?"

"Look at the thickness of the sides and look at the lid. Why, it's five inches through. And see that great metal spring across it."

"That's for holding the lid up," said the mate. "You see, it won't lean back. What's that German printing on the inside?"

"It means that it was made by Johann Rothstein of Augsburg, in 1606."

"And a solid bit of work, too. But it doesn't throw much light on what has passed, does it, Captain Barclay? That candlestick looks like gold. We shall have something for our trouble after all."

He leant forward to grasp it, and from that moment I have never doubted as to the reality of inspiration, for on the instant I caught him by the collar and pulled him straight again. It may have been some story of the Middle Ages which had come back to my mind, or it may have been that my eye had caught some red which was not that of rust upon the upper part of the lock, but to him and to me it will always seem an inspiration, so prompt and sudden was my action.

"There's devilry here," said I. Give me the crooked stick from the corner."

It was an ordinary walking-cane with a hooked top. I passed it over the candlestick and gave it a pull. With a flash a row of polished steel fangs shot out from below the upper lid, and the great striped chest snapped at us like a wild animal. Clang came the huge lid into its place, and the glasses on the swinging rack sang and tinkled with the shock. The mate sat on the edge of the table and shivered like a frightened horse.

"You've saved my life, Captain Barclay!" said he.

So this was the secret of the striped treasure-chest of old Don Ramirez di Leyra, and this was how he preserved his ill-gotten gains from the Terra Firma and the Province of Veraquas. Be the thief ever so cunning he could not tell that golden candlestick from the other articles of value, and the instant that he laid hand upon it the terrible spring was unloosed and the murderous steel spikes were driven into his brain, while the shock of the blow sent the victim backwards and enabled the chest to automatically close itself. How many, I wondered, had fallen victims to the ingenuity of the Mechanic of Augsburg. And as I thought of the possible history of that grim striped chest my resolution was very quickly taken.

"Carpenter, bring three men and carry this on deck."

"Going to throw it overboard, sir?"

"Yes, Mr. Allardyce. I'm not superstitious as a rule, but there are some things which are more than a sailor can be called upon to stand."

"No wonder that brig made heavy weather, Captain Barclay, with such a thing on board. The glass is dropping fast, sir, and we are only just in time."

So we did not even wait for the three sailors, but we carried it out, the mate, the carpenter, and I, and we pushed in with our own hands over the bulwarks. There was a white spout of water, and it was gone. There it lies, the striped chest, a thousand fathoms deep, and if, as they say, the sea will some day be dry land, I grieve for the man who finds that old box and tries to penetrate into its secret.

● *The Right Honourable gentleman is indebted to his memory for his jests, and to his imagination for his facts.*
(Richard Brinsley Sheridan)

MOVING

MOVING PIECES

*The Miracle Car, God at Work, A New Engine
are three separate extracts from God's Smuggler.

● *Certainly, I must confess my own barbarousnes, I never heard the olde song of "Percy and Duglas" that I found not my heart mooved more than with a Trumpet.*

(Sir Philip Sidney)

THE CLOUDED SKY
Anonymous 1

In the year 1826, John Turner's glowing picture of "Cologne" was shown at the Royal Academy. It was hung between two portraits both by Thomas Lawrence which was unfortunate as the rich bright colours of Turner's picture could only serve to lessen the effect of both the ones beside. Lawrence himself was most upset, and complained bitterly, but was told it was too late now to move the pictures around.

On the morning of the opening of the exhibition, many of Turner's admirers made haste to see the "Cologne" painting about which they heard so much. They paused, puzzled. There was no golden sky now: it was a dull colour. One man hurried to Turner and cried, "What has happened to your picture?"

Turner drew him aside. "Don't worry," he said. "Poor Lawrence was so unhappy. It's only lamp black. It'll all wash off after the exhibition."

MR VALIANT-FOR-TRUTH
from "Pilgrim's Progress" 1½
by John Bunyan

After this, it was noised abroad that Mr *Valiant-for-truth* was taken with a summons by the same post as the other; and had this for a token that the summons was true, *That his pitcher was broken at the fountain.* When he understood it, he called for his friends, and told them of it. Then said he, "I am going to my Father's; and though with great difficulty I am got hither, yet now I do not repent me of all the trouble I have been at, to arrive where I am. My sword I give to him that shall succeed me in my pilgrimage, and my courage and skill to him that can get it. My marks and scars I carry with me, to be a witness for me that I have fought his battles who now will be my rewarder." When the day that he must go hence was come, many accompanied him to the river side, into which, as he went he said, *"Death, where is thy sting?"* And as he went deeper, he said, *"Grave, where is thy victory?"* So he passed over, and all the trumpets sounded for him on the other side.

from
ULYSSES

by Alfred, Lord Tennyson   2

The aging Ulysses, bored with inactivity at home, proposes one final voyage.

> *There lies the port: the vessel puffs her sail:*
> *There gloom the dark broad seas. My mariners,*
> *Souls that have toil'd, and wrought, and thought with me—*
> *That ever with a frolic welcome took*
> *The thunder and the sunshine, and opposed*
> *Free hearts, free foreheads—you and I are old;*
> *Old age hath yet his honour and his toil;*
> *Death closes all: but something ere the end,*
> *Some work of noble note, may yet be done,*
> *Not unbecoming men that strove with Gods.*
> *The lights begin to twinkle from the rocks:*
> *The long day wanes: the slow moon climbs: the deep*
> *Moans round with many voices. Come, my friends,*
> *'Tis not too late to seek a newer world.*
> *Push off, and, sitting well in order, smite*
> *The sounding furrows; for my purpose holds*
> *To sail beyond the sunset, and the baths*
> *Of all the western stars, until I die.*
> *It may be that the gulfs will wash us down:*
> *It may be we shall touch the happy isles,*

And see the great Achilles, whom we knew.
Tho' much is taken, much abides; and tho'
We are not now that strength which in old days
Moved earth and heaven; that which we are, we are;
One equal temper of heroic hearts,
Made weak by time and fate, but strong in will
To strive, to seek, to find, and not to yield.

from
ODE ON INTIMATIONS
OF IMMORTALITY
by William Wordsworth   2

There was a time when meadow, grove, and stream,
The earth, and every common sight,
       To me did seem
     Apparelled in celestial light,
The glory and the freshness of a dream.
It is not now as it hath been of yore;—
     Turn wheresoe'er I may,
       By night or day,
The things which I have seen I now can see no more.

     The Rainbow comes and goes,
     And lovely is the Rose,
     The Moon doth with delight
Look round her when the heavens are bare,
     Waters on a starry night
     Are beautiful and fair;
The sunshine is a glorious birth;
But yet I know, where'er I go,
That there hath pass'd away a glory from the earth.

Our birth is but a sleep and a forgetting:
The Soul that rises with us, our life's star,
Hath had elsewhere its setting,
And cometh from afar:
Not in entire forgetfulness,
And not in utter nakedness,
But trailing clouds of glory do we come
From God, who is our home:
Heaven lies about us in our infancy!

Shades of the prison-house begin to close
Upon the growing boy,
But He beholds the light, and whence it flows,
He sees it in his joy;
The Youth who daily farther from the east
Must travel, still is Nature's Priest,
And by the vision splendid
Is on his way attended;
At length the Man perceives it die away,
And fade into the light of common day.

THE MIRACLE CAR

See page 193   3

GOD AT WORK

See page 194   3

A NEW ENGINE

See page 196   4

All three are from "God's Smuggler"
by Brother Andrew

THE HUNT

from "Black Beauty" 5½
by Anna Sewell

Black Beauty himself is the storyteller.

Before I was two years old, a circumstance happened which I have never
forgotten. It was early in the spring; there had been a little frost in the night,
and a light mist still hung over the plantations and meadows. I and the other
colts were feeding at the lower part of the field when we heard, quite in the
distance, what sounded like the cry of dogs. The oldest of the colts raised his
head, pricked his ears, and said, "There are the hounds!" and immediately
cantered off, followed by the rest of us to the upper part of the field, where
we could look over the hedge and see several fields beyond. My mother, and
an old riding horse of our master's were also standing near, and seemed to
know all about it.

"They have found a hare," said my mother, "and if they come this way,
we shall see the hunt."

And soon the dogs were all tearing down the field of young wheat next to
ours. I never heard such a noise as they made. They did not bark, nor howl,
nor whine, but kept on a "yo, o, o! yo, o, o!" at the top of their voices.

After them came a number of men on horseback, some of them in green
coats, all galloping as fast as they could. The old horse snorted and looked
eagerly after them, and we young colts wanted to be galloping with them, but
they were soon away in the fields lower down; here it seemed as if they had
come to a stand; the dogs left off barking, and ran about every way with their
noses to the ground.

"They have lost the scent," said the old horse; "perhaps the hare will get
off."

"What hare?" I said.

"Oh! I don't know *what* hare; likely enough it may be one of our own
hares out of the plantation; any hare they can find will do for the dogs and
men to run after;" and before long the dogs began their "yo! yo, o, o!" again,
and back they came altogether at full speed, making straight for our meadow
at the part where the high bank and hedge overhang the brook.

"Now we shall see the hare," said my mother; and just then a hare wild with fright rushed by, and made for the plantation. On came the dogs, they burst over the bank, leapt the stream, and came dashing across the field followed by the huntsmen. Six or eight men leaped their horses clean over, close upon the dogs. The hare tried to get through the fence; it was too thick, and she turned sharp round to make for the road, but it was too late; the dogs were upon her with wild cries; we heard one shriek, and that was the end of her. One of the huntsmen rode up and whipped off the dogs, who would soon have torn her to pieces. He held her up by the leg torn and bleeding, and all the gentlemen seemed well pleased.

As for me, I was so astonished that I did not at first see what was going on by the brook; but when I did look, there was a sad sight; two fine horses were down, one was struggling in the stream, and the other was groaning on the grass. One of the riders was getting out of the water covered with mud, the other lay quite still.

"His neck is broke," said my mother.

"And serve him right, too," said one of the colts.

I thought the same, but my mother did not join with us.

"Well! no," she said, "you must not say that; but though I am an old horse, and have seen and heard a great deal, I never yet could make out why men are so fond of this sport; they often hurt themselves, often spoil good horses, and tear up the fields, and all for a hare or a fox, or a stag, that they could get more easily some other way; but we are only horses, and don't know."

Whilst my mother was saying this, we stood and looked on. Many of the riders had gone to the young man; but my master, who had been watching what was going on, was the first to raise him. He head fell back and his arms hung down, and every one looked very serious. There was no noise now; even the dogs were quiet, and seemed to know that something was wrong. They carried him to our master's house. I heard afterwards that it was young George Gordon, the Squire's only son, a fine, tall young man, and the pride of his family.

There was now riding off in all directions to the doctor's, to the farrier's, and no doubt to Squire Gordon's, to let him know about his son. When Mr. Bond, the farrier, came to look at the black horse that lay groaning on the grass, he felt him all over, and shook his head; one of his legs was broken. Then some one ran to our master's house and came back with a gun; presently there was a loud bang and a dreadful shriek, and then all was still;

the black horse moved no more.

My mother seemed much troubled; she said she had known that horse for years, and that his name was "Rob Roy"; he was a good bold horse, and there was no vice in him. She never would go to that part of the field afterwards.

Not many days after, we heard the church bell tolling for a long time; and looking over the gate we saw a long strange black coach that was covered with black cloth and was drawn by black horses; after that came another and another and another, and all were black, while the bell kept tolling, tolling. They were carrying young Gordon to the churchyard to bury him. He would never ride again. What they did with Rob Roy I never knew; but 'twas all for one little hare.

THE LAST DAYS
from "Scott's Last Expedition"   7
by Robert Falcon Scott

Friday 16 March or Saturday 17: Lost track of dates, but think the last correct. Tragedy all along the line. At lunch, the day before yesterday, poor Titus Oates said he couldn't go on; he proposed we should leave him in his sleeping-bag. That we could not do, and we induced him to come on, on the afternoon march. In spite of its awful nature for him he struggled on and we made a few miles. At night he was worse and we knew the end had come.

Should this be found I want these facts recorded. Oates's last thoughts were of his mother, but immediately before he took pride in thinking that his regiment would be pleased with the bold way in which he met his death. We can testify to his bravery. He has borne intense suffering for weeks without complaint, and to the very last was able and willing to discuss outside subjects. He did not — would not — give up hope till the very end. He was a brave soul. This was the end. He slept through the night before last, hoping not to wake; but he woke in the morning — yesterday. It was blowing a blizzard. He said, "I am just going outside and may be some time." He went out into the blizzard and we have not seen him since.

I take this opportunity of saying that we have stuck to our sick companions the last. In case of Edgar Evans, when absolutely out of food and he lay insensible, the safety of the remainder seemed to demand his abandonment, but Providence mercifully removed him at this critical moment. He died a natural death, and we did not leave him till 2 hours after his death. We knew that poor Oates was walking to his death, but though we tried to dissuade him, we knew it was the act of a brave man and an English gentleman. We all hope to meet the end with similar spirit, and assuredly the end is not far.

I can only write at lunch and then only occasionally. The cold is intense, $-40°$ at midday. My companions are unendingly cheerful, but we are all on the verge of serious frost-bites, and though we constantly talk of fetching through I don't think any one of us believes it in his heart.

We are cold on the march now, and at all times except meals. Yesterday we had to lay up for a blizzard and today we move dreadfully slowly. We are at No 14 pony camp, only two pony marches from One Ton Depot. We leave here our theodolite, a camera, and Oates's sleeping-bags. Diaries, etc, and geological specimens carried at Wilson's special request, will be found with us or on our sledge.

Sunday 18 March: Today, lunch, we are 21 miles from the depot. Ill fortune presses, but better may come. We have had more wind and drift from ahead yesterday; had to stop marching; wind NW, force 4, temp. $-35°$. No human being could face it, and we are worn out *nearly*.

My right foot has gone, nearly all the toes — two days ago I was proud possessor of best feet. These are the steps of my downfall. Like an ass I mixed a small spoonful of curry powder with my melted pemmican — it gave me violent indigestion. I lay awake and in pain all night; woke and felt done on the march; foot went and I didn't know it. A very small measure of neglect and have a foot which is not pleasant to contemplate. Bowers takes first place in condition, but there is not much to choose after all. The others are still confident of getting through — or pretend to be — I don't know! We have the last *half* fill of oil in our primus and a very small quantity of spirit — this alone between us and thirst. The wind is fair for the moment, and that is perhaps a fact to help. The mileage would have seemed ridiculously small on our outward journey.

Monday 19 March: Lunch. We camped with difficulty last night, and were dreadfully cold till after our supper of cold pemmican and biscuit and a half a pannikin of cocoa cooked over the spirit. Then, contrary to expectation, we got warm and all slept well. Today we started in the usual dragging manner. Sledge dreadfully heavy. We are 15½ miles from the depot and ought to get there in 3 days. What progress! We have two day's food, but barely a day's fuel. All our feet are getting bad – Wilson's best, my right foot worst, left all right. There is no chance to nurse one's feet till we can get hot food into us. Amputation is the least I can hope for now, but will the trouble spread? That is the serious question. The weather doesn't give us a chance – the wind from N to NW and –40° temp. today.

Wednesday 21 March: Got within 11 miles of depot Monday night; had to lay up all yesterday in severe blizzard. Today forlorn hope, Wilson and Bowers going to depot for fuel.

Thursday 22 and 23 March: Blizzard bad as ever – Wilson and Bowers unable to start – tomorrow last chance – no fuel and only one or two of food left – must be near the end. Have decided it shall be natural – we shall march for the depot with or without our effects and die in our tracks.

Thursday 29 March: Since the 21st we have had a continuous gale from WSW and SW. We had fuel to make two cups of tea apiece and bare food for 2 days on the 20th. Every day we have been ready to start for our depot 11 *miles* away, but outside the door of the tent it remains a scene of whirling drift. I do not think we can hope for any better things now. We shall stick it out to the end, but we are getting weaker, of course, and the end cannot be far.

It seems a pity, but I do not think I can write more.

R. SCOTT

Last entry:
For God's sake look after our people.

● *For books are not absolutely dead things, but do contain a potency of life in them to be as active as that soul was whose progeny they are.*
(John Milton)

G

SNAPSHOT OF A DOG

by James Thurber   9½

I ran across a dim photograph of him the other day, going through some old
things. He's been dead twenty-five years. His name was Rex (my brothers and
I named him when we were in our early teens) and he was a bull terrier."An
American bull terrier," we used to say, proudly; none of your English bulls.
He had one brindle eye that sometimes made him look like a clown and
sometimes reminded you of a politician with derby hat and cigar. The rest of
him was white except for a brindle saddle that always seemed to be slipping
off and a brindle stocking on a hind leg. Nevertheless, there was a nobility
about him. He was big and muscular and beautifully made. He never lost his
dignity even when trying to accomplish the extravagant tasks my brothers
and myself used to set for him. One of these was the bringing of a ten-foot
wooden rail into the yard through the back gate. We would throw it out into
the alley and tell him to go get it. Rex was as powerful as a wrestler, and
there were not many things that he couldn't manage somehow to get hold of
with his great jaws and lift or drag to wherever he wanted to put them, or
wherever we wanted them put. He could catch the rail at the balance and lift
it clear of the ground and trot with great confidence toward the gate. Of
course, since the gate was only four feet wide or so, he couldn't bring the rail
in broadside. He found that out when he got a few terrific jolts, but he
wouldn't give up. He finally figured out how to do it, by dragging the rail,
holding onto one end, growling. He got a great, wagging satisfaction out of his
work. We used to bet kids who had never seen Rex in action that he could
catch a baseball thrown as high as they could throw it. He almost never let us
down. Rex could hold a baseball with ease in his mouth, in one cheek, as if it
were a chew of tobacco.

He was a tremendous fighter, but he never started fights. I don't believe he
liked to get into them, despite the fact that he came from a line of fighters. He
never went for another dog's throat but for one of its ears (that teaches a dog
a lesson), and he would get his grip, close his eyes, and hold on. He could
hold on for hours. His longest fight lasted from dusk until almost pitch-dark,
one Sunday. It was fought in East Main Street in Columbus with a large,
snarly nondescript that belonged to a coloured man. When Rex finally got his

ear grip, the brief whirlwind of snarling turned to screeching. It was frightening to listen to and to watch. The Negro boldly picked the dogs up somehow and began swinging them around his head, and finally let them fly like a hammer in a hammer throw, but although they landed ten feet away with a great plump, Rex still held on.

The two dogs eventually worked their way to the middle of the car tracks, and after a while two or three streetcars were held up by the fight. A motorman tried to pry Rex's jaws open with a switch rod; somebody lighted a fire and made a torch of a stick and held that to Rex's tail, but he paid no attention. In the end, all the residents and storekeepers in the neighbourhood were on hand, shouting this, suggesting that. Rex's joy of battle, when battle was joined, was almost tranquil. He had a kind of pleasant expression during fights, not a vicious one, his eyes closed in what would have seemed to be sleep had it not been for the turmoil of the struggle. The Oak Street Fire Department finally had to be sent for − I don't know why nobody thought of it sooner. Five or six pieces of apparatus arrived, followed by a battalion chief. A hose was attached and a powerful stream of water was turned on the dogs. Rex held on for several moments more while the torrent buffeted him about like a log in a freshet. He was a hundred yards away from where the fight started when he finally let go.

The story of that Homeric fight got all around town, and some of our relatives looked upon the incident as a blot on the family name. They insisted that we get rid of Rex, but we were very happy with him, and nobody could have made us give him up. We would have left town with him first, along any road there was to go. It would have been different, perhaps if he'd ever started fights, or looked for trouble. But he had a gentle disposition. He never bit a person in the ten strenuous years that he lived, nor ever growled at anyone except prowlers. He killed cats, that is true, but quickly and neatly and without especial malice, the way men kill certain animals. It was the only thing he did that we could never cure him of doing. He never killed, or even chased, a squirrel. I don't know why. He had his own philosophy about such things. He never ran barking after wagons or automobiles. He didn't seem to see the idea in pursuing something you couldn't catch, or something you couldn't do anything with, even if you did catch it. A wagon was one of the things he couldn't tug along with his mighty jaws, and he knew it. Wagons, therefore, were not a part of his world.

Swimming was his favourite recreation. The first time he ever saw a body of water (Alum Creek), he trotted nervously along the steep bank for a while, fell to barking wildly, and finally plunged in from a height of eight feet or more. I shall always remember that shining, virgin dive. Then he swam upstream and back just for the pleasure of it, like a man. It was fun to see him battle upstream against a stiff current, struggling and growling every foot of the way. He had as much fun in the water as any person I have known. You didn't have to throw a stick in the water to get him to go in. Of course, he would bring back a stick to you if you did throw one in. He would even have brought back a piano if you had thrown one in.

That reminds me of the night, way after midnight, when he went a-roving in the light of the moon and brought back a small chest of drawers that he found somewhere — how far from the house nobody ever knew; since it was Rex, it could easily have been half a mile. There were no drawers in the chest when he got it home and it wasn't a good one — he hadn't taken it out of anybody's house; it was just an old cheap piece that somebody had abandoned on a trash heap. Still, it was something he wanted, probably because it presented a nice problem in transportation. It tested his mettle. We first knew about his achievement when, deep in the night, we heard him trying to get the chest up onto the porch. It sounded as if two or three people were trying to tear the house down. We came downstairs and turned on the porch light. Rex was on the top step trying to pull the thing up, but it had caught somehow and he was just holding his own. I suppose he would have held his own till dawn if we hadn't helped him. The next day we carted the chest miles away and threw it out. If we had thrown it out in a nearby alley, he would have brought it home again, as a small token of his integrity in such matters. After all, he had been taught to carry heavy wooden objects about, and he was proud of his prowess.

I am glad that Rex never saw a trained police dog jump. He was just an amateur jumper himself, but the most daring and tenacious I have ever seen. He would take on any fence we pointed out to him. Six feet was easy for him, and he could do eight by making a tremendous leap and hauling himself over finally by his paws, grunting and straining; but he lived and died without knowing that twelve- and sixteen-foot walls were too much for him. Frequently, after letting him try to go over one for a while, we would have to carry him home. He would never have given up trying.

There was in his world no such thing as the impossible. Even death couldn't beat him down. He died, it is true, but only, as one of his admirers said, after 'straight-arming the death angel' for more than an hour. Late one afternoon he wandered home, too slowly and too uncertainly to be the Rex that had trotted briskly homeward up our avenue for ten years. I think we all knew when he came through the gate that he was dying. He had apparently taken a terrible beating, probably from the owner of some dog that he had got into a fight with. His head and body were scarred. His heavy collar with the teeth marks of many a battle on it was awry; some of the big brass studs in it were sprung loose from the leather. He licked at our hands and, staggering, fell, but got up again. We could see that he was looking for someone. One of his three masters was not home. He did not get home for an hour. During that hour the bull terrier fought against death as he had fought against the cold, strong current of Alum Creek, as he had fought to climb twelve-foot walls. When the person he was waiting for did come through the gate, whistling, ceasing to whistle, Rex walked a few wobbly paces toward him touched his hand with his muzzle, and fell down again. This time he didn't get up.

from
GOD'S SMUGGLER
by Brother Andrew 10
[3 + 3 + 4]

Brother Andrew devoted himself to bringing copies of the Bible to Christians behind the Iron Curtain.

THE MIRACLE CAR 3

The roads in Yugoslavia were extraordinarily hard on cars. When we weren't climbing fierce mountain trails, we were fording steams at the bottom of steep valleys.

But the worst threat to the little V.W. was the dust. Dust lay over the unpaved roads like a shroud; it sifted in on us even through the closed windows, and I hated to think what it was doing to the engine. Every morning in our Quiet Time, Nikola and I would include a prayer for the car.

"Lord, we don't have either the time or the money for repairs on the car, so will You please keep it running?"

One of the peculiarities of travel in Yugoslavia in 1957 was the friendly road-stoppings that took place. Cars, especially foreign cars, were still such a rarity that when two drivers passed each other, they almost always stopped to exchange a few words about road conditions, weather, gasoline supplies, bridges. One day we were dusting along a mountain road when up ahead we spotted a small truck coming towards us. As it pulled alongside, we also stopped.

"Hello," said the driver. "I believe I know who you are. You're the Dutch missionary who is going to preach in Terna tonight."

"That's right."

"And this is the Miracle Car?"

"The Miracle Car?"

"I mean the car that you pray for each morning."

I had to laugh. I had mentioned the prayer in a previous meeting, and the word had obviously gone on ahead. "Yes," I admitted, "this is the car."

"Mind if I take a look at her? I'm a mechanic."

"I'd appreciate it." I had put gasoline in that engine, and that was literally all since I had crossed the border. The mechanic went around to the rear and lifted the hood over the motor. For a long time he stood there, just staring.

"Brother Andrew," he said at last, "I have just become a believer. It is mechanically impossible for this engine to run. Look. The air filter. The carburettor. The sparks. No, I'm sorry. This car cannot run."

"And yet it's taken us thousands of miles."

The mechanic only shook his head. "Brother," he said, "would you permit me to clean your engine for you and give you a change of oil? It hurts me to see you abuse a miracle."

Gratefully we followed the man to his village a few miles from Terna. We pulled behind him into a little courtyard filled with pigs and geese. That night while we preached he took the engine apart, cleaned it piece by piece, changed the oil, and by the time we were ready to leave the next morning, presented us with a grinning new automobile. God had answered our prayer.

GOD AT WORK   3

It took me four hours to get across the Rumanian border. When I pulled up to the checkpoint on the other side of the Danube, I said to myself, "Well,

I'm in luck. Only half a dozen cars. This will go swiftly."

When forty minutes had passed and the first car was still being inspected, I thought, "Poor fellow, they must have something on him to take so long."

But when that car finally left and the next inspection took half an hour too, I began to worry. Literally everything that family was carrying had to be taken out and spread on the ground. Every car in the line was put through the same routine. The fourth inspection lasted for well over an hour. The guards took the driver inside and kept him there while they removed hub caps, took his engine apart, removed seats.

"Dear Lord," I said, as at last there was just one car ahead of me, "what am I going to do? Any serious inspection will show up those Rumanian Bibles right away.

"Lord," I went on, "I know that no amount of cleverness on my part can get me through this border search. Dare I ask for a miracle? Let me take some of the Bibles out and leave them in the open where they will be seen. Then, Lord, I cannot possibly be depending on my own stratagems, can I? I will be depending utterly upon You."

While the last car was going through its chilling inspection, I managed to take several Bibles from their hiding places and pile them on the seat beside me.

It was my turn. I put the little V.W. in low gear, inched up to the officer standing at the left side of the road, handed him my papers, and started to get out. But his knee was against the door, holding it closed. He looked at my photograph in the passport, scribbled something down, shoved the papers back under my nose, and abruptly waved me on.

Surely thirty seconds had not passed. I started the engine and inched forward. Was I supposed to pull over, out of the way, where the car could be taken apart? Was I . . . surely I wasn't . . . I coasted forward, my foot poised above the brake. Nothing happened. I looked out the rear mirror. The guard was waving the next car to a stop, indicating to the driver that he had to get out. On I drove a few more yards. The guard was having the driver behind me open the hood of his car. And then I was too far away to doubt that indeed I had made it through that incredible checkpoint in the space of thirty seconds.

My heart was racing. Not with the excitement of the crossing, but with the excitement of having caught such a spectacular glimpse of God at work.

A NEW ENGINE   4

I was on one of these trips that year that the courageous little car engine breathed its last.

It happened in West Germany. I was on my way home from a trip to East Germany and Poland. With me in the car were two Dutch boys I had picked up in Berlin, students who had spent their Easter vacation working in the refugee camps. At five o'clock one afternoon we were spinning along, when suddenly there was a crackling sound in the rear of the car and the engine died.

We coasted to a stop and opened the little door in the rear, but nothing we could do would make it start again.

Then I straightened up and saw that beside the road, at the spot where the car's own momentum had deposited us, was an emergency telephone box. I picked up the receiver and asked for a tow truck. Within twenty minutes we were all bending over the engine with the manager of the service garage.

He inspected the various parts in silence for some minutes, then walked forward and looked at the odometer [= *milometer*].

"Ninety-seven thousand kilometres," he read aloud. His puzzled frown had not left him. "It's a good mileage, of course, and yet unless you've been over unusually rough terrain . . ."

Now I saw what was bothering him. A little shamefacedly I admitted that the odometer had long since reached its maximum reading of 99,999 and flipped over the zero mark again: this was the second time it had registered ninety-seven thousand.

"Then I should say," said the manager, wiping the oil from his hands, "that you've got your money's worth. That engine just hasn't any more to give."

"How long would it take to put in a new one?"

He stopped to consider. "My crew leaves in ten minutes. They could have a new engine in for you in an hour, but you'd have to pay them a good tip for staying overtime."

"How much would the whole thing cost, including the tip?"

"Five hundred marks."

Without hesitation I said, "Go ahead. I'll go and get some more money changed at the train station."

It was on board the streetcar going to the station that I counted my money and realised that all I had with me would not make five hundred marks. There'd be no help from the two students back at the garage: they were riding with me in the first place because they were flat broke. Should I go back and cancel the work order? No. I could see God's hand too clearly in all of this. Stopping precisely at the emergency telephone, having the engine wear out here in Germany where it came from, rather than in some distant and hostile spot where replacements would have been impossible and questions awkward. I was far too familiar with the way Christ looks after the practical side of the ministry to miss these signs. This was all His timing, and the question of the money was also in His hands. I was not worried, just fascinated to see how He was going to work it all out.

When I had changed every last guilder, it came — with the Germany money in my pocket — to 470 marks. Fifty shy of the amount I needed to pay the bill and to buy gasoline on the way home.

"Well," I said to myself, "something will happen on the streetcar going back."

But nothing did. I got the garage to find the workmen just finishing up and my two passengers nowhere to be seen. They'd gone for a walk, one of the men said, packing away his tools. The others were cleaning up too. I could delay the moment of reckoning no longer.

And at that instant, the two young Dutchmen raced through the door, one of them waving something in his hand. "Andy!" he shouted. "Craziest thing ever happened to me! We were just walking along the street when this lady came up to us and asked if we were Dutchmen. When I said yes, she gave me this bill! She said God wanted us to have it!"

The bill was for fifty marks.

● *Oxford is on the whole more attractive than Cambridge to the ordinary visitor; and the traveller is therefore recommended to visit Cambridge first, or to omit it altogether if he cannot visit both.*
(Karl Baedeker)

THE GIFT OF THE MAGI

by O. Henry   13½
                                                         [11]

Note: the Magi = the Wise Men

One dollar and eighty-seven cents. That was all. And sixty cents of it was in pennies. Pennies saved one and two at a time by bulldozing the grocer and the vegetable man and the butcher until one's cheeks burned with the silent imputation of parsimony that such close dealing implied. Three times Della counted it. One dollar and eight-seven cents. And the next day would be Christmas.

There was clearly nothing to do but flop down on the shabby little couch and howl. So Della did it. Which instigates the moral reflection that life is made up of sobs, with sniffles predominating.

[While the mistress of the home is gradually subsiding from the first stage to the second, take a look at the home. A furnished flat at $8 per week. It did not exactly beggar description, but it certainly had that word on the lookout for the mendicancy squad.

In the vestibule below was a letter-box into which no letter would go, and an electric button from which no mortal finger could coax a ring. Also appertaining thereunto was a card bearing the name "Mr. James Dillingham Young."

The "Dillingham" had been flung to the breeze during a former period of prosperity when its possessor was being paid $30 per week. Now, when the income was shrunk to $20, the letters of "Dillingham" looked blurred, as though they were thinking seriously of contracting to a modest and unassuming D. But whenever Mr. James Dillingham Young came home and reached his flat above he was called "Jim" and greatly hugged by Mrs. James Dillingham Young, already introduced to you as Della. Which is all very good.]

Della finished her cry and attended to her cheeks with the powder rag. She stood by the window and looked out dully at a gray cat walking a gray fence in a gray backyard. Tomorrow would be Christmas Day, and she had only $1.87 with which to buy Jim a present. She had been saving every penny she could for months, with this result. Twenty dollars a week doesn't go far. Expenses had been greater than she had calculated. They always are. Only

$1.87 to buy a present for Jim. Her Jim. Many a happy hour she had spent planning for something nice for him. Something fine and rare and sterling – something just a little bit near to being worthy of the honor of being owned by Jim.

[There was a pier-glass between the windows of the room. Perhaps you have seen a pier-glass in an $8 flat. A very thin and very agile person may, by observing his reflection in a rapid sequence of longitudinal strips, obtain a fairly accurate conception of his looks. Della, being slender, had mastered the art.]

Suddenly she whirled from the window and stood before the glass. Her eyes were shining brilliantly, but her face had lost its color within twenty seconds. Rapidly she pulled down her hair and let it fall to its length.

Now, there were two possessions of the James Dillingham Youngs in which they both took a mighty pride. One was Jim's gold watch that had been his father's and his grandfather's. The other was Della's hair. [Had the Queen of Sheba lives in the flat across the airshaft, Della would have let her hair hang out the window some day to dry just to depreciate Her Majesty's jewels and gifts. Had King Solomon been the janitor, with all his treasures piled up in the basement, Jim would have pulled out his watch every time he passed, just to see him pluck at his beard from envy.]

So now Della's beautiful hair fell about her rippling and shining like a cascade of brown waters. It reached below her knee and made itself almost a garment for her. And then she did it up again nervously and quickly. Once she faltered for a minute and stood still while a tear or two splashed on the worn red carpet.

On went her old brown jacket; on went her old brown hat. With a whirl of skirts and with the brilliant sparkle still in her eyes, she fluttered out the door and down the stairs to the street.

Where she stopped the sign read: "Mme. Sofronie. Hair Goods of All Kinds." One flight up Della ran, and collected herself, panting. Madame, large, too white, chilly, hardly looked the "Sofronie."

"Will you buy my hair?" asked Della.

"I buy hair," said Madame. "Take yer hat off and let's have a sight at the looks of it."

Down rippled the brown cascade.

"Twenty dollars," said Madame, lifting the mass with a practised hand.

"Give it to me quick," said Della.

Oh, and the next two hours tripped by on rosy wings. Forget the hashed metaphor. She was ransacking the stores for Jim's present.

She found it at last. It surely had been made for Jim and no one else. There was no other like it in any of the stores, and she had turned all of them inside out. It was a platinum fob chain simple and chaste in design, property proclaiming its value by substance alone and not by meretricious ornamentation — as all good things should do. It was even worthy of The Watch. As soon as she saw it she knew that it must be Jim's. It was like him. Quietness and value — the description applied to both. Twenty-one dollars they took from her for it, and she hurried home with the 87 cents. With that chain on his watch Jim might be properly anxious about the time in any company. Grand as the watch was, he sometimes looked at it on the sly on account of the old leather strap that he used in place of a chain.

When Della reached home her intoxication gave way a little to prudence and reason. She got our her curling irons and lighted the gas and went to work repairing the ravages made by generosity added to love. Which is always a tremendous task, dear friends — a mammoth task.

Within forty minutes her head was covered with tiny, close-lying curls that made her look wonderfully like a truant schoolboy. She looked at her reflection in the mirror long, carefully, and critically.

"If Jim doesn't kill me," she said to herself, "before he takes a second look at me, he'll say I look like a Coney Island chorus girl. But what could I do — oh! what could I do with a dollar and eighty-seven cents?"

At 7 o'clock the coffee was made and the frying-pan was on the back of the stove hot and ready to cook the chops.

Jim was never late. Della doubled the fob chain in her hand and sat on the corner of the table near the door that he always entered. Then she heard his step on the stair away down the first flight, and she turned white for just a moment. She had a habit of saying little silent prayers about the simplest everyday things, and now she whispered: "Please God, make him think I am still pretty."

The door opened and Jim stepped in and closed it. He looked thin and very serious. Poor fellow, he was only twenty-two — and to be burdened with a family! He needed a new overcoat and he was without gloves.

Jim stopped inside the door, as immovable as a setter at the scent of quail. His eyes were fixed upon Della, and there was an expression in them that she could not read, and it terrified her. It was not anger, nor surprise, nor disapproval, nor horror, nor any of the sentiments that she had been prepared for. He simply stared at her fixedly with that peculiar expression on his face.

Della wriggled off the table and went for him.

"Jim, darling," she cried, "don't look at me that way. I had my hair cut off and sold it because I · couldn't have lived through Christmas without giving you a present. It'll grow out again — you won't mind, will you? I just had to do it. My hair grows awfully fast. Say 'Merry Christmas!' Jim, and let's he happy. You don't know what a nice — what a beautiful, nice gift I've got for you."

"You've cut off your hair?" asked Jim, laboriously, as if he had not arrived at that patent fact yet even after the hardest mental labor.

"Cut it off and sold it," said Della. "Don't you like me just as well, anyhow? I'm me without my hair, ain't I?"

Jim looked at the room curiously.

"You say your hair is gone?" he said, with an air almost of idiocy.

"You needn't look for it," said Della. "It's sold, I tell you — sold and gone. too. It's Christmas Eve, boy. Be good to me, for it went for you. Maybe the hairs of my head were numbered," she went on with a sudden serious sweetness, "but nobody could ever count my love for you. Shall I put the chops on, Jim?"

[Out of his trance Jim seemed quickly to wake. He enfolded his Della. For ten seconds let us regard with discreet scrutiny some inconsequential object in the other direction. Eight dollars a week or a million a year — what is the difference? A mathematician or a wit would give you the wrong answer. The magi brought valuable gifts, but that was not among them. This dark assertion will be illuminated later on.]

Jim drew a package from his overcoat pocket and threw it upon the table.

"Don't make any mistake, Dell," he said, "about me. I don't think there's anything in the way of a haircut or a shave or a shampoo that could make me like my girl any less. But if you'll unwrap that package you may see why you had me going a while at first."

White fingers and nimble tore at the string and paper. And then an ecstatic scream of joy; and then, alas! a quick feminine change to hysterical tears and wails, necessitating the immediate employment of all the comforting powers of the lord of the flat.

For there lay The Combs — the set of combs, side and back, that Della had worshipped for long in a Broadway window. Beautiful combs, pure tortoise shell, with jewelled rims — just the shade to wear in the beautiful vanished hair. They were expensive combs, she knew, and her heart had simply craved and yearned over them without the least hope of possession. And now, they were hers, but the tresses that should have adorned the coveted adornments were gone.

But she hugged them to her bosom, and at length she was able to look up with dim eyes and a smile and say: "My hair grows so fast, Jim!"

And then Della leaped up like a little singed cat and cried: "Oh, oh!"

Jim had not yet seen his beautiful present. She held it out to him eagerly upon her open palm. The dull precious metal seemed to flash with a reflection of her bright and ardent spirit.

"Isn't it a dandy, Jim? I hunted all over town to find it. You'll have to look at the time a hundred times a day now. Give me your watch. I want to see how it looks on it."

Instead of obeying, Jim tumbled down on the couch and put his hands under the back of his head and smiled.

"Dell," said he, "let's put our Christmas presents away and keep 'em a while. They're too nice to use just at present. I sold the watch to get the money to buy your combs. And now suppose you put the chops on."

The magi, as you know, were wise men — wonderfully wise men — who brought gifts to the Babe in the manger. They invented the art of giving Christmas presents. Being wise, their gifts were no doubt wise ones, possibly bearing the privilege of exchange in case of duplication. And here I have lamely related to you the uneventful chronicle of two foolish children in a flat who most unwisely sacrificed for each other the greatest treasures of their house. But in a last word to the wise of these days let it be said that of all who give gifts these two were the wisest. Of all who give and receive gifts, such as they are wisest. Everywhere they are the wisest. They are the magi.

● *We are none of us infallible — not even the youngest of us.*
(William Hepworth Thompson)

THE NIGHTINGALE AND THE ROSE

by Oscar Wilde   14½

[13]

'She said she would dance with me if I brought her red roses,' cried the young Student, 'but in all my garden there is no red rose.'

From her nest in the holm-oak tree the Nightingale heard him, and she looked out through the leaves and wondered.

'No red rose in all my garden!' he cried, and his beautiful eyes filled with tears. 'Ah, on what little things does happiness depend! I have read all that the wise men have written, and all the secrets of philosophy are mine, yet for want of a red rose is my life made wretched.'

'Here at last is a true lover,' said the Nightingale. 'Night after night have I sung of him though I knew him not: night after night have I told his story to the stars and now I see him. His hair is dark as the hyacinth-blossom, and his lips are red as the rose of his desire, but passion has made his face like pale ivory and sorrow has set her seal upon his brow.'

'The Prince gives a ball tomorrow night,' murmured the young Student, 'and my love will be of the company. If I bring her a red rose she will dance with me till dawn. If I bring her a red rose, I shall hold her in my arms, and she will lean her head upon my shoulder and her hand will be clasped in mine. But there is no red rose in my garden, so I shall sit lonely and she will pass me by. She will have no heed of me, and my heart will break.'

['Here, indeed, is the true lover,' said the Nightingale. 'What I sing of, he suffers: what is joy to me, to him is pain. Surely love is a wonderful thing. It is more precious than emeralds and dearer than fine opals. Pearls and pomegranates cannot buy it, nor is it set forth in the market-place. It may not be purchased of the merchants, nor can it be weighed out in the balance for gold.'

'The musicians will sit in their gallery,' said the young Student, 'and play upon their stringed instruments, and my love will dance to the sound of the harp and the violin. She will dance so lightly that her feet will not touch the floor, and the courtiers in their gay dresses will throng round her. But with me she will not dance, for I have no red rose to give her';] and he flung himself down on the grass, and buried his face in his hands, and wept.

['Why is he weeping?' asked a little Green Lizard, as he ran past him with his tail in the air.

'Why, indeed?' said a Butterfly, who was fluttering about after a sunbeam.

'Why, indeed?' whispered a Daisy to his neighbour, in a soft low voice.

'He is weeping for a red rose,' said the Nightingale.

'For a red rose?' they cried; 'how very ridiculous!' and the little Lizard, who was something of a cynic, laughed outright.

But] the Nightingale understood the secret of the Student's sorrow, and she sat silent in the oak-tree, and thought about the mystery of Love.

Suddenly she spread her brown wings for flight, and soared into the air. She passed through the grove like a shadow and like a shadow she sailed across the garden.

In the centre of the grass-plot was standing a beautiful rose-tree, and when she saw it she flew over to it, and lit upon a spray.

'Give me a red rose,' she cried, 'and I will sing you my sweetest song.'

But the Tree shook its head.

'My roses are white,' it answered; 'as white as the foam of the sea, and whiter than the snow on the mountain.But go to my brother who grows round the old sun-dial, and perhaps he will give you what you want.'

So the Nightingale flew over to the Rose-tree that was growing round the old sun-dial.

'Give me a red rose,' she cried, 'and I will sing you my sweetest song.'

But the Tree shook its head.

'My roses are yellow,' it answered; 'as yellow as the hair of the mermaiden who sits upon an amber throne, and yellower than the daffodil that blooms in the meadow before the mower comes with his scythe. But go to my brother who grows beneath the Student's window, and perhaps he will give you what you want.'

So the Nightingale flew over the the Rose-tree that was growing beneath the Student's window.

'Give me a red rose,' she cried, 'and I will sing you my sweetest song.'

But the Tree shook its head.

'My roses are red,' it answered; 'as red as the feet of the dove, and redder than the great fans of coral that wave and wave in the ocean-cavern. But the winter has chilled my veins, and the frost has nipped my buds, and the storm has broken my branches, and I shall have no roses at all this year.'

'One red rose is all I want,' cried the Nightingale, 'only one red rose! Is there no way by which I can get it?'

'There is a way,' answered the Tree; 'but it is so terrible that I dare not tell it to you.'

'Tell it to me,' said the Nightingale, 'I am not afraid.'

'If you want a red rose,' said the Tree, 'you must build it out of music by moonlight, and stain it with your own heart's-blood. You must sing to me with your breast against a thorn. All night long you must sing to me, and the thorn must pierce your heart, and your life-blood must flow into my veins and become mine.'

'Death is a great price to pay for a red rose,' cried the Nightingale, 'and Life is very dear to all. It is pleasant to sit in the green wood, and to watch the Sun in his chariot of gold, and the Moon in her chariot of pearl. Sweet is the scent of the hawthorn, and sweet are the bluebells that hide in the valley, and the heather that blows on the hill. Yet Love is better than Life, and what is the heart of a bird compared to the heart of a man?'

So she spread her brown wings for flight, and soared into the air. She swept over the garden like a shadow, and like a shadow she sailed through the grove.

The young Student was still lying in the grass, where she had left him, and the tears were not yet dry in his beautiful eyes.

'Be happy,' cried the Nightingale, 'be happy; you shall have your red rose. I will build it out of music by moonlight, and stain it with my own heart's-blood. All that I ask of you in return is that you will be a true lover, [for Love is wiser than Philosophy, though he is wise, and mightier than Power, though he is mighty. Flame-coloured are his wings, and coloured like flames is his body. His lips are sweet as honey, and his breath is like frankincense.']

The Student looked up from the grass, and listened, but he could not understand what the Nightingale was saying to him, for he only knew the things that are written down in books.

But the Oak-tree understood, and felt sad, for he was very fond of the little Nightingale who had built her nest in his branches.

'Sing me one last song,' he whispered; 'I shall feel lonely when you are gone.'

So the Nightingale sang to the Oak-tree, and her voice was like water bubbling from a silver jar.

When she had finished her song, the Student got up, and pulled a note-book and a lead-pencil out of his pocket.

'She has form,' he said to himself, as he walked away through the grove — 'that cannot be denied to her; but has she got feeling? I am afraid not. In fact, she is like most artists; she is all style without any sincerity. She would not sacrifice herself for others. [She thinks merely of music, and everybody knows that the arts are selfish. Still, it must be admitted that she has some beautiful notes in her voice. What a pity it is that they do not mean anything, or do any practical good!'] And he went to his room, and lay down on his little pallet-bed, and began to think of his love; and, after a time, he fell asleep.

And when the moon shone in the heavens the Nightingale flew to the Rose-tree, and set her breast against the thorn. All night long she sang, with her breast against the thorn, and the cold crystal Moon leaned down and listened. All night long she sang, and the thorn went deeper and deeper into her breast, and her life-blood ebbed away from her.

She sang first of the birth of love in the heart of a boy and a girl. And on the topmost spray of the Rose-tree there blossomed a marvellous rose, petal following petal, as song followed song. Pale was it, at first, as the mist that hangs over the river — pale as the feet of the morning, and silver as the wings of the dawn. As the shadow of a rose in a mirror of silver, as the shadow of a rose in a water-pool, so was the rose that blossomed on the topmost spray of the Tree.

But the Tree cried to the Nightingale to press closer against the thorn. 'Press closer, little Nightingale,' cried the Tree, 'or the Day will come before the rose is finished.'

So the Nightingale pressed closer against the thorn, and louder and louder grew her song, for she sang of the birth of passion in the soul of a man and a maid.

And a delicate flush of pink came into the leaves of the rose, like the flush in the face of the bridegroom when he kisses the lips of the bride. But the thorn had not yet reached her heart, so the rose's heart remained white, for only a Nightingale's heart's-blood can crimson the heart of a rose.

And the Tree cried to the Nightingale to press closer against the thorn. 'Press closer, little Nightingale,' cried the Tree, 'or the Day will come before the rose is finished.'

So the Nightingale pressed closer against the thorn, and the thorn touched her heart, and a fierce pang of pain shot through her. Bitter, bitter was the pain, and wilder and wilder grew her song, for she sang of the Love that is perfected by Death, of the Love that dies not in the tomb.

And the marvellous rose became crimson, like the rose of the eastern sky. Crimson was the girdle of petals, and crimson as a ruby was the heart.

But the Nightingale's voice grew fainter, and her little wings began to beat, and a film came over her eyes. Fainter and fainter grew her song, and she felt something choking in her throat.

Then she gave one last burst of music. The white Moon heard it, and she forgot the dawn, and lingered on in the sky. The red rose heard it, and it trembled all over with ecstasy, and opened its petals to the cold morning air. Echo bore it to her purple cavern in the hills, and woke the sleeping shepherds from their dreams. It floated through the reeds of the river, and they carried its messages to the sea.

'Look, look!' cried the Tree, 'the rose is finished now'; but the Nightingale made no answer, for she was lying dead in the long grass, with the thorn in her heart.

And at noon the Student opened his window and looked out.

'Why, what a wonderful piece of luck!' he cried; 'here is a red rose! I have never seen any rose like it in all my life. It is so beautiful that I am sure it has a long Latin name'; and he leaned down and plucked it.

Then he put on his hat, and ran up to the Professor's house with the rose in his hand.

The daughter of the Professor was sitting in the doorway winding blue silk on a reel, and her little dog was lying at her feet.

'You said that you would dance with me if I brought you a red rose,' cried the Student. 'Here is the reddest rose in all the world. You will wear it tonight next your heart, and as we dance together it will tell you how I love you.'

But the girl frowned.

'I am afraid it will not go with my dress,' she answered; 'and besides, the Chamberlain's nephew has sent me some real jewels, and everybody knows that jewels cost far more than flowers.'

'Well, upon my word, you are very ungrateful,' said the Student angrily; and he threw the rose into the street, where it fell into the gutter, and a cart-wheel went over it.

'Ungrateful!' said the girl. 'I tell you what, you are very rude; and, after all, who are you? Only a Student. Why, I don't believe you have even got silver buckles to your shoes as the Chamberlain's nephew has'; and she got up from her chair and went into the house.

'What a silly thing Love is!' said the Student as he walked away. 'It is not half as useful as Logic, for it does not prove anything, and it is always telling one of things that are not going to happen, and making one believe things that are not true. In fact, it is quite unpractical, and, as in this age to be practical is everything, I shall go back to Philosophy and study Metaphysics.'

So he returned to his room and pulled out a great dusty book, and began to read.

NICKY'S STORY
from "The Cross and the Switchblade"   17
by David Wilkerson (with John & Elizabeth Sherrill)

Rev. Wilkerson takes one of the boys from the streets of Brooklyn back to his home parish.

So that was how Nicky came to be standing on a platform in Elmira, New York, a few weeks later, to relate the story of his life. I had spent some time on his introduction, stressing the poverty and loneliness that spawned boys like this so that the audience would not judge him too harshly before they heard him through.

My precautions were unnecessary. From the moment he began to speak, that roomful of people was with him. His own words, the pathetic narrowness of his experience — for all he was so knowing — the flat, staccato recital by a boy who had not learned to exaggerate or embellish, told more than volumes [of sociology] about the world he came from.

"I was mostly in the streets," he began, "because my parents had customers coming where we lived. They would come at night or in the day and then all of us kids had to go out. They were spiritualists, my parents. They advertised in the Spanish papers that they would talk with the dead and cure sickness, and they would also give advice about money and family problems.

"There was only one room at home, so us kids were in the street. At first the other kids beat me up and I was afraid all the time. Then I learned how to fight and they were scared of me and they left me alone. After a while I got so I liked it better in the street than I did at home. At home I was the youngest one. I was nothing. But in the street they knew who I was.

"My family moved a lot and mostly it was on account of me. If there was any trouble the police would come around asking questions and then the superintendent where we lived would go to my parents and say we had to move. They didn't want their building to have trouble with the police. It was that way if the police just asked a Puerto Rican boy a question. It didn't matter if he did anything, the minute the police came around asking about him, he and his family had to get out.

"I didn't know why I acted like I did. There was a thing inside me that scared me. It worried me all the time but I couldn't stop it. It was this feeling I got if I saw a cripple. It was a feeling like I wanted to kill him. It was that way with blind people, too, or real little kids — anyone weak or hurt — I would hate them.

"One day I told my old man about this thing. We never talked or anything, but this thing scared me. So I told him and he said I had a devil. He tried to call the devil out of me, but it wouldn't come.

"The crazy thing in me got worse and worse. If someone had crutches I would kick them or if an old man had a beard I would try to pull it out and I would rough up little kids. And all the while I would be scared and wanting to cry, but the thing inside me was laughing and laughing. The other thing was blood. The minute I saw blood I would begin to laugh and I couldn't stop it.

"When we moved into the Fort Green Projects, I went in with the Mau Maus. They wanted me to be President. But in a rumble the President has to direct traffic (give orders) and I wanted to fight. So they made me Vice-President.

"I was also Sergeant-at-Arms. That meant I was in charge of the arsenal. We had garrison belts and bayonets and switchblades and zip guns. I liked to go in and just look at those things. You steal a car aerial to make the zip guns. You use a door latch for the trip hammer and they shoot .22 shells.

"But for the rumbling I liked a baseball bat. I'd cut a hole in a garbage can to see out, then I'd put it over my head and swing the bat. The Mau Maus would never fight alongside me because when I got crazy like that I would beat on anybody.

"I also learned how to stick with a knife, which is when you cut someone but don't kill him. I stuck sixteen people, and I was in jail twelve times. Some of those times my picture was in the paper. When I walked down the street everyone knew me and the mothers would call their little kids.

"The gangs knew me too. One day when I was waiting for a subway five guys came up behind me. They got a leather belt around my neck and kept twisting it. I didn't die, but I used to wish I had because after that I could never talk right. There was a funny note in my throat. I had this hate of people who had anything wrong with them, and now it was me. I had to bop all the time, after that, to keep respect.

"Our gang controlled the turf as far as Coney Island and Ralph Avenue. We had red jackets with MM on them and we wore continental heels, which are good in a fight. One day we were in a candy store on Flatbush Avenue. There were six of us, drinking soda, when seven Bishops walked in. The Bishop gang was at war with the Mau Maus.

"One of the Bishops went up to the candy counter like he owned it. My boys were watching me. I walked over and I shoved him. He shoved back and then everyone was fighting. The owner's wife started screaming. All the other customers ran out on the sidewalk. There was a butcher knife on the counter. One of my boys picked it up and cut a Bishop five times through the scalp. I saw the blood and I started to laugh. I knew he was dead and I was scared but I couldn't stop laughing. The owner's wife was telephoning the police. Another one of my boys picked up that butcher knife and hit her right in the stomach. Then we ran.

"I never touched the knife so I didn't go to jail. But my parents had to go to the court and I guess it was the first time they looked at me. They got scared when they saw what I was. They decided to get out of New York and go back to Puerto Rico. My brother and I went to the airport to say good-bye to them. On the way back from the airport in his car he gave me a .32 pistol. He said, 'You're on your own, Nick.'

"The first thing I had to do was to find a place to sleep. I held up a guy with the gun and got ten dollars. I rented a room on Myrtle Avenue. I was sixteen then. That's how I lived after that, holding up guys for money or something to hock.

"During the day it was all right. I was with the gang. Whatever the President and I told them to do they would do. But at night, when I had to go into that room, it was terrible. I would think about the two dead people in the candy store. I would bang my head on the floor to stop thinking about them. I started waking up in the middle of the night, crying for my mother.

We never talked, or anything, before she left, but suddenly I felt like she should come and take care of me.

"I turned eighteen in July, 1958. That month the Dragons from the Red Hook projects killed one of our boys. We were going down on the subway to get one of them. That's gang law: if one Mau Mau dies, one Dragon dies. We were walking down Edward Street on our way to the subway station when we saw a police car stopped and a whole bunch of Chaplains hanging around. The Chaplains are the Nigger gang in Fort Greene. We had a treaty with them that we wouldn't fight and we would work together if another gang invaded us.

"It looked like action so we went over. The Chaplains were all standing around two guys I never seen, one had a bugle and the other was a real skinny guy. Then somebody brought an American flag and the police car drove away. All it was, the two guys wanted to hold a street meeting.

"As soon as the flag came the skinny guy got up on a chair, opened up a book, and this is what he read out of it:

For God so loved the world that He gave His only begotten Son, that whosoever believeth in Him should not perish.

" 'Now,' the preacher said, 'I'm going to talk to you about "Whosoever". "Whosoever" means Negroes and Puerto Ricans, and especially it means gang members. Do you know that when they crucified Jesus they crucified gang members, too? One on each side of Him . . .'

"I'd had enough. I said, 'Come on you guys, we got business.'

"Not one of them moved. It was the first time they didn't follow me. Then I got scared and I called that preacher every filthy name I knew. He paid no attention, just kept on talking, a long time.

"And the next thing you knew the President of the Chaplains flopped down on his knees, right on Edward Street, and started crying. The Vice-President and two War Lords got down beside him and they cried. One thing I couldn't stand was crying. I was glad when the Chaplains left. I figured we would go too.

"But then this preacher comes up to Israel — he was President of the Mau Maus — and starts shaking his hand. I figured he was trying to bust us up and I went up and shoved the preacher. Israel stared at me like he'd never seen me before.

"So that preacher heads for me. 'Nicky', he said, 'I love you.'

"No one in my life ever told me that. I didn't know what to do. 'You come near me, preacher,' I said, 'I'll kill you!' And I meant it. Well, Israel and the preacher talked some more, but at last he left and I thought it was over. Only we never went after the Dragons.

"But later this preacher came back and he talked about this big meeting for gangs they were going to have up in Manhattan, and how we should come. 'We'd like to come, Preach,' says Israel, 'but how we going to get through Chink town?' 'I'll send a bus for you,' says the preacher. So then Israel said we'll come.

"Well, I said, not me. I felt like I'd rather die than go to that meeting. But when the gang went it turned out I was with them. I was scared not to be with the gang. I figured I would fix his little prayer-meeting for him. When we got there here were three rows of seats right down front roped off for us. That surprised me some. The preacher said he'd save us seats but I never figured he'd do it.

"A lady was playing the organ and I got the guys stamping and shouting for action. Then a little girl came out on stage and began to sing. I whistled at her and everyone laughed. It was all going my way and I was feeling good.

"Finally the preacher came out and he said, 'Before the message tonight we're going to take up a collection.'

"Well I figured I saw his angle. I'd been wondering all along what was in this for him. Now I saw he was a money-grabber like everyone else.

" 'We're going to ask the gang members themselves to take it up,' he says. They'll bring the money around behind this curtain and up onto the stage.'

"I figured he didn't have any good sense; anyone could see there was a door back there!

"May I have six volunteers?' he says.

"Man, I was on my feet in a second. I pointed out five of my boys and we piled down there quick. Here was my chance to make him look silly. He gave us cardboard cartons. I wanted to get started right away but he made us stand there while he reeled off a long blesssing. I tried not to laugh.

"Well, we worked that whole arena. If I didn't like what someone put in, I just stood there till he gave me some more. They all knew Nicky. Then we met down behind the curtain.

"There was the door. It was wide open. I could see street lights and I heard a water truck spraying the street. Back in the arena some of them were laughing. They knew what we were pulling. My boys were watching me, waiting the word to cut out.

"And I just stood there. I didn't know what it was; I had a funny feeling.

Suddenly I knew what it was: that preacher trusted me. That never happened in my life before and I just stood there, my boys watching me.

"Inside, I could hear they were giving him a hard time. They were shouting and stamping and he having to stand there and face them, trusting me.

" 'All right, you guys,' I said. 'We're going up on that stage.'

"They looked at me like I wasn't right in my head, but they never argued. I was that kind of a guy that the other kids didn't argue with. We went up the stairs and you never heard a place get so quiet so fast. We gave him the cartons. 'Here's your money, Preacher,' I said.

"He just took the money, not surprised or anything, like he knew all the time I'd bring it.

"Well, I went back to my seat and I was thinking harder than I ever thought before. He started talking and it was all about the Holy Spirit. The preacher said the Holy Spirit could get inside people and make them clean. He said it didn't matter what they'd done, the Holy Spirit could make them start new, like babies.

"Suddenly I wanted that so bad I couldn't stand it. It was as if I was seeing myself for the first time. All the filth and the hate and the foulness like pictures in front of my eyes.

" 'You can be different!' he said. 'Your life can be changed!'

"I wanted that, I needed that, but I knew it couldn't happen to me. The preacher told us to come forward if we wanted to be changed but I knew it was no use for me.

"Then Israel told us all to get up. 'I'm President,' he said, 'and this whole gang is going up there!'

"I was the first one at the rail. I kneeled down and said the first prayer of my life and this was it: 'Dear God, I'm the dirtiest sinner in New York. I don't think You want me. If You do want me, You can have me. As bad as I was before, I want to be that good for Jesus.'

"Later the preacher gave me a Bible and then I went home wondering if the Holy Ghost was really inside me, and how I would know. The first thing that happened, when I went into my room and shut the door I didn't feel scared. I felt like I had company in the room — not God or anyone like that, but the way I'd feel if my mother came back. I had four pot sticks (marijuana cigarettes) in my pocket. I ripped them up and threw them out the window.

"The next day everyone was staring because word had gone around that Nicky had religion. But another thing happened that made me know it was real. Little kids would always run when they saw me, but on that day two

little boys stared at me a minute and then they came right up to me. They
wanted me to measure and see which one of them was the taller — nothing
important. Only I put my arms around them because I knew then I was
different, even if it didn't show except to kids.

"Then a few weeks later, a Dragon came up to me and he said, 'Is it true
you don't carry weapons any more?' I told him it was true, and he pulled a
ten-inch knife and went for my chest. I threw my hand up and caught the
knife there. I don't know why, but he ran, and I stood there, looking at the
blood coming from my hand. I remembered how blood always made me go
crazy, but that day it didn't. Words came into my mind that I had read in my
Bible, 'The blood of Jesus Christ cleanseth us from all sin.' I ripped my shirt
and tied up my hand and from that day blood never bothered me."

As Nicky talked, a hush fell over the room — the scarcely breathing silence
that invariably attends a miracle. For we were witnessing a miracle — or hearing
one — that night in Elmira, and as each of the listeners took it in, he caught
his breath with the little gasp that sends the knowledge racing through the
room.

Nicky's voice, the straining, painful, stammering voice in which he had
begun his story, had altered as he spoke. Gradually the words came more
readily, the sounds clearer, until he was speaking as distinctly and effortlessly
as anyone in the room. Only now had Nicky himself realized it. He stood on
the platform trembling, unable to go on, tears streaming down his face.

I never knew what had caused his speech problem, whether it was physical
injury resulting from the strangling, or what doctors term "hysterical"
affliction. Nicky, of course, never in his wildest fancies considered seeing a
doctor about it. I only know that, from that night on, his voice was healed.

That night, too, a collection was taken in Elmira which started Nicky on a
long and remarkable journey.

● For this relief, much thanks.